CHOOSE THE

Happiness Habit

PAM GOLDEN

Roedway Press ✦ La Quinta, California

Copy editing by Ruel Nolledo
Interior design by Sara Patton
Back cover copy by Susan Kendrick
Printed in the United States of America

ISBN 0-9659650-7-4
Library of Congress Number 97-75408

This book is available at special quantity discounts to use as premiums, in promotions, or for training programs.

*This book is dedicated to
Ed and Albertine Roed,
who not only chose the
happiness habit, but gave it
to all who surrounded them.*

Contents

WORKBOOK
Section 1

Section 2

The one unifying thread through all human endeavor is the quest for happiness. To be happy is, perhaps, the only common objective shared by all people in all ages.

– Benjamin Franklin, *The Art of Virtue*
Edited by George L. Rogers

Are you as happy as you want to be right now?

Do you have moments of happiness every day
of your life?

The answer to that question is very important,
because it has been scientifically proven
that if you are not happy *today* you will not
be happy tomorrow — unless you take
steps to change today.

If you think you could be happier than you are
right now, then this program is for you.

Happiness is not something that comes to us.

It is something we create now, today.

Waiting for something to change in order to
be happy is waiting to live your life.

If you have only one life, month, week, or
moment to live, let it be a happy one, a
joyous expression of the gift of life.

Mission Happiness

The search for happiness is one of the most important issues of our time. Never before in history has it been so possible yet so absent.

At a time when we could be dancing in the streets, rejoicing over the incredible accomplishments of this century, we are having an epidemic of depression.

The mission of the program described in these pages is to revolutionize the way we live our lives, so that we live as an expression of our happiness instead of endlessly chasing it.

By taking responsibility for our personal happiness, we create an environment that has a ripple effect. Like depression, happiness affects everything it touches.

People who are optimistic accomplish more and lead healthier lives.

Creating your own happiness and experiencing all the joy that life has to offer is one of the most important things you can do for yourself, your family, and everyone you touch. Start today by choosing the happiness habit and spreading joy everywhere you go.

The happiness habit
is the spirit of joy in being alive.
It is being at peace with yourself,
accepting who you are,
just the way you are.

It is knowing that there are
both good and bad in life
but choosing to focus on the good.

It is consistently appreciating
and celebrating
the good about yourself,
what you do, who you are,
the people in your life, your community,
your world, the future.

It is not ignoring problems,
but facing and solving them
instead of being consumed by them.

It is choosing to be happy instead of "right."

It is making the world a better place
for your having been here.

The happiness habit
is recognizing moments of happiness
every single day
no matter what the circumstances.

Preface

Several years ago my friend's 90-year-old mother passed away. Her last words to her daughter summed up how she felt about life. She turned to her daughter and said, "Everything is bullshit!" Can you imagine what it must feel like to live for almost an entire century and end up feeling that way?

After everything you've seen, everything you've done, everything you've experienced—was life worth living at all? Maybe it wasn't. For a short time this thought gave me a lot of freedom. After all, if everything is nonsense, then why not just have a good time, live for the moment?

All that changed suddenly a few years ago. My father had to undergo two major surgeries in the span of 24 hours. One of those operations involved an open heart procedure. By the end of it, he was in very bad shape. There was a very real possibility that his next breath would be his last.

My family and I kept vigil over him in those difficult hours following surgery. It was hard to watch my wonderful, dynamic father lying helpless in the hospital bed with countless tubes coming out of his body. He was in pain, and barely able to move, yet there was nothing I could do to help.

My 27-year-old daughter was visibly shaken by her grandfather's condition. As she stood over him, tears rolling down her cheeks, she gripped his hand, as if to send energy into the body of her beloved Poppa.

Then, suddenly, he opened his eyes. When he saw her red, tear-covered face, he squeezed her hand and struggled to lift his head. "Don't feel bad," he said gently. "I've lived a very good life."

My father did not always feel that way. At one time in his life he was a hopeless drunk. He lost his job, deserted his family, and ended up living in a packing crate on the outskirts of Las Vegas. He was at the bottom of the bottom. Whenever he could scrape up enough change, he'd waste it on liquor. Then he would crawl into his "home" and feel sorry for himself while he guzzled his life away.

When he was 43 years old, he began to take charge of his life. He joined a 12-step program and worked his way back to sobriety, putting everything he had into it. The change was miraculous. A man who seemed destined to die a pitiful, hopeless alcoholic became a much loved and admired man who inspired thousands of people to live productive lives.

Many people live their lives without challenging their circumstances. My father, determined to actively create his life, worked and struggled every day, and succeeded in becoming the person he wanted to be.

My purpose in writing *Choose the Happiness Habit* is to provide a method or system for creating happiness, for taking charge of your life like my father did. It's easy to use. It works. This program will help you create true happiness in your life.

Love, Pam Golden

Acknowledgments

More than 20 years ago, Lola Lopez, a dear friend, asked me to speak with a group of disadvantaged youths about how to give an effective job interview. I'll never forget the excitement I felt when those young people stood up in front of a group of people and talked about their great qualities. You could see their self-esteem come bubbling through their smiles as they did things they had never done before. Later, I asked them how being in the workshop had made a difference in their lives. My favorite comment was, "It took all the shy out of me!"

Since then I have been on a dedicated mission to find ways to provide people with skills that will put them in charge of their lives. It was only recently that I finally found a method for providing people with an effective yet simple way to create their own happiness—one that didn't require the hours of personal instruction and demonstration that go into the courses I present to corporations.

It all came together one day when I was watching that remarkable, inspirational woman, Oprah Winfrey. She was interviewing Sarah Ban Breathnach about her book, *Simple Abundance,* and what I had been working on for years suddenly came together. At last I was able to create the HabitBuilder, a tool for developing the most important habit of all: the "happiness habit."

It has taken a lot of work from many people over the years for this to all come together in one moment in time. I wish to express my gratitude and appreciation to the following people who made this book possible:

✦ My husband, John O'Keefe, whose relentless optimism and faith in me inspired me to continued action. He patiently read and reread and reread this manuscript and offered many wise and useful comments. He has also brought me more happiness than I ever knew was possible.

✦ My wonderful daughter, Amber, who lights up my life. She has tirelessly read and commented on version after version of this book, and she is always there when I need her. I am thrilled that the techniques in this book have helped her increase her own happiness.

✦ My sister, Sandy Sims, a writer who has given much of her heart and her time. She always responded to my panicked requests for help and made time when she had none. Her valuable comments on this book helped me to make sense when I didn't!

✦ Keith Raskin, my son-in-law, who offered perceptive and detailed comments and a cheerful willingness to help.

✦ Len Randall, a shrewd businessman with a loving heart and generous spirit, who taught me much about how to deal with people.

✦ Janet Keefe, who made sure I was always working at a place where it made a difference and has brought much joy to my life. Her warm heart and vitality give life to whatever she does.

✦ The dedicated and committed authors who have provided inspiration, information, and techniques for the making the world a better place. Though I have not met them, I count on them as trusted advisors. The authors I have relied on most are:

Martin E.P. Seligman, Ph.D., an extraordinary person whose books have provided the world with pathways to taking control of one's life.

Mihayl Csikszentmihayli, whose research into what makes people happy and identification of the principles of "flow" have given people tools to enjoy life.

Stephen Covey, whose *Seven Habits of Highly Effective People* is a well-used, well-worn, invaluable reference for me. His work has brought a sense of values to the world.

Daniel Goleman, whose book, *Emotional Intelligence*, finally explains the vital importance of emotional skills.

David Myers, who wrote the most thoroughly re-searched and documented book on happiness that's ever been written. It is a fountain of information. His touches of humor are unexpected and delightful.

Susan Jeffers, Ph.D., who enthusiastically embraces optimism and shows people how to not let fear get in their way.

Scott Peck, whose realistic approach to life and prob-lems allows effective action.

Peter Senge, who brings not just systems, but passion and heart to business.

Dale Carnegie, whose *How to Win Friends and Influence People* was the first self-help book I ever read.

Finally, I am grateful to:

✦ The Southern California Training Council, for being a great company with a strong commitment, and providing me with some of the most wonderful places to make a difference through my work.

✦ Wendie Willson and Marcia Ishibashi-Ito, for all of their help in the beginning of this project.

✦ Ruell "Magic Fingers" Nolledo, for the sparkle and structure he has given.

✦ Carol Hartman, for capturing the essence of a message in the fewest possible words.

✦ Sara Patton, for her patience, love of the English language, commitment to excellence, and warm and generous spirit.

✦ Nancy Upshaw, for her invaluable help.

Why This Book?

Every year a growing number of self-help books are published. Many of these wonderful books provide guidance for solving your problems, inspiration on how to achieve your fondest dreams, help in developing your innate talents, and tools and techniques for creating your world the way you want it to be. You'd think with all this wonderful information we'd all be much happier, but we aren't. An alarming number of people who read these books continue to live lives of "quiet desperation," unable to make desired changes in the condition of their lives. Why is this? Why can't we simply apply the principles suggested in the books, thereby improving our lives and the lives of those around us?

Martin Seligman gives us some insight into this problem in his book, *The Optimistic Child*. He says, "Pessimism is an entrenched habit of mind that has sweeping and disastrous consequences: depressed mood, resignation, underachievement, and even unexpectedly poor physical health. Pessimism is not shaken in the natural course of life's ups and downs. Rather, it hardens with each setback and soon becomes self-fulfilling." He also says, "One of the most significant findings in psychology in the last 20 years is that individuals can choose the way they think." And the way we think will determine our actions, which in turn will determine our happiness.

Changing "entrenched" habits calls for powerful change methods. Methods that fit into our harried and hurried lives. Methods that compel us to continue using them because we see results.

My aunt Sherry says, "You can't just read a cookbook and expect dinner to be done." Nor can you simply read a book and expect change to happen. You need to have a program that incorporates discipline over time, because discipline and time are critical to changing entrenched habits.

I learned this through personal experience. As a teenager, I was always very shy around strangers. Even as an adult, I would go to parties and spend all night either hiding out behind the buffet table or talking with my husband for fear that I would actually have to speak with people I didn't know. I had no idea what to say. I admired the way others carried on such animated conversations and wished I knew their secret. Having little control over my predicament was very depressing.

One day while driving home after a particularly difficult social situation, I pulled off to the side of the road and began sobbing uncontrollably. I felt helpless. I was 26 years old. I wanted so badly to be involved in the world, but I didn't know what to do.

In the midst of my tears, I remembered that after my father-in-law Eddy had taken a course in public speaking, he became a very friendly, outgoing person. Right then I decided that if Eddy could make that change, so could I! I wiped my tears away, started the car, and drove to the nearest bookstore to buy a book on public speaking. (No way was I going to take a class. Yikes! I might have to get up and speak in front of people!)

What happened after that was, for me, nothing short of a miracle. First, I learned how to listen. Then I learned how to speak to people. Soon I could draw anyone into a conversation and, as a result, I began to look forward to meeting new people. For the first time I had control over my life. I was no longer a helpless victim!

With my success in using a self-help book, I began to wonder what made my situation different. Why was I able to make such a profound change when I saw so many others who couldn't? As I considered this, I realized that I had, without being aware of it, developed a method for applying new information in my daily life. A systematic method that I used to create a new habit to replace my old habit.

As my aunt Sherry says, "There's a lot that goes on between reading a recipe and sitting down to a delicious meal." The same with self-help books and classes. There's a lot that has to happen between learning what to do and achieving results.

Today I teach management, leadership, problem-solving, and people skills to corporate personnel. A few years ago, the most frustrating part of my job was to see students get very engaged in and enthusiastic about the course, then walk out the door and not apply their learning in their everyday lives. Why? What kept them from implementing what they had learned?

I realized that I needed to develop tools, so my clients could make the lasting positive changes they wanted. I decided to experiment with the same method I had used when I was trying to overcome my shyness. Thus, the HabitBuilder was born.

When participants used the HabitBuilder they began to find continuity from one class to the next. They maintained their excitement and were eager to share their outside-of-class success stories.

When my dad had recovered from his surgeries he initially found it very difficult to apply himself to his postoperative walking exercises. I showed him my system and how to apply it to his program. Using the HabitBuilder motivated my father to follow his exercise program. Instead of sitting in his chair when I came over, he would enthusiastically get up to demonstrate his progress.

To let go of entrenched, nonproductive habits and create habits that will take you to your life's desire, you must practice your new habits. The HabitBuilder is a 90-day program designed to provide you with an easy, motivational method for doing just that.

Our Right to Pursue Happiness

We hold these truths to be self-evident: that all people are created equal, that they are endowed by their Creator with certain inalienable rights, that among these are life, liberty, and the pursuit of happiness . . .

Recognize those words? Of course you do. They're part of the Declaration of Independence, that historic document on which our country was founded. The men who signed this piece of paper were risking everything for these principles. "Our lives, our fortunes, and our sacred honor," they pledged, and in so doing the United States of America was born.

The Declaration of Independence is not some casual commitment written by "spin doctors" out to win a few votes for their candidate or get out of a tight spot. By putting their names down on this document, these men were putting their lives at risk. Unless the newly formed United States won the war, the Congressmen would be branded traitors by the English government. And everyone knew what happened to a traitor under English law.

5

"The victim could be strangled, drawn, or disemboweled, while still alive. His entrails were then burned and his body quartered."[1]

All this for what? What in heaven's name could be so important that people were willing to risk strangulation and other tortures, not to mention certain death? Sure, one can understand the need to fight for ideals such as all people are created equal and have the right to life and liberty. But happiness? Why that?

Think about it for a moment. In most countries back then (and even today in a few places) no government cared if a person was happy, much less whether they had a *right* to pursue happiness. You would be laughed out of the British Court for even suggesting such a ridiculous notion. As things stood, you knew your lot in life, you did what you had to do, and you were going to darn well put up with it, whatever the case. A happy life? Get real!

Then a small group of people slowly realized that there had to be a better way of doing things. Surely there had to be more to life than just suffering through each day. That radical thought grew into a revolution that is still making its presence felt today. You and I are part of that revolution. A very important part.

This book is about happiness, something important enough to be one of the key elements in the Declaration of Independence. It might help us to define exactly what

---

[1] Diane Ravitch. *The American Reader*. New York: Harper Collins, 1990.

happiness is. Some people believe that it's a feeling. But if it's only a feeling, can't we achieve this through alcohol, or drugs, or even on a roller coaster ride? Perhaps, but it's not likely that Jefferson or Washington were thinking of that when they drafted the Declaration of Independence. Can you see them willing to risk life and limb for a joy ride or a kegger party? I think not.

No, happiness to them had to have been something more substantial, more elemental to their lives as human beings. It was something that originated inside each and every individual.

If you're like most people, you may already consider yourself pretty happy. But we mean more than that. *The American Heritage Dictionary* defines happiness as "a condition of supreme well-being and good spirits...joy, cheer, cheerfulness, gladness, beatitude, blessedness."

Yes, happiness is a condition of supreme well-being, good spirits, and cheerfulness. It's also being at peace with yourself because you know you've done your best. It is accepting and rejoicing in who you are. It's experiencing joy in simply being alive. The happiness we are talking about is having your life be a wonderful adventure, a way of living that will cause us to proclaim with pride, joy, and passion, "I've lived a good life!"

The Happiness Chase

What is it that makes your life a wonderful adventure? To look at what brings happiness, we must first understand what doesn't bring happiness.

"Money doesn't buy happiness." You've heard it. I've heard it. We've all heard it. And when we hear it, we nod our heads wisely and say, "How true." But the fact is that people flock to anything that promises to make them rich. We eagerly embrace get-rich-quick schemes and buy lottery tickets by the millions. Our paychecks keep the gambling casinos flourishing.

We live in the most affluent time in the history of the world. Many of today's "poor" families have more possessions than the average family had just 20 years ago. We have computers, VCRs, color televisions, air conditioners, dishwashers, microwaves, one or more cars, and instant communication via the Internet. Our choice of goods, services, and entertainment is astounding.

Yet we are in the midst of an epidemic of depression. Alcoholism and fear of violence touch each of us in our daily lives. We are losing the war on drugs, as children are using drugs at younger and younger ages. Our crime rate is the highest among developed nations. At any moment someone we love could be gunned down in school, on the job, on the freeway, or in a restaurant. And it's been true for years that more than half of all marriages end in divorce; the rate is even higher for second marriages. Why? Why are our lives filled with fear, uncertainty, and anxiety? Why aren't we happy?

We are unhappy because we are chasing the wrong things. We think something outside of ourselves will bring us happiness. We think winning is "being the one with the most toys." If we are only popular enough, rich enough, thin enough, have the right job, or are good-looking enough, we will live happily ever after.

We are bombarded every day with television, radio, newspapers, and magazines telling us that "things" will solve our problems and make us happy. All we need to do is get them. So we do. We chase after wealth, cars, clothes, and all the newest gadgets in search of the brass ring.

We will *never* find happiness that way! In fact, when we chase after things—all in an effort to feel good—we insulate ourselves from what *does* bring happiness. We become addicted to the adrenaline rush and confuse the momentary high of a new possession with the true happiness that comes from being at peace with yourself, and taking pride in who you are.

Not only do money and possessions not bring happiness, but there is astonishing evidence to prove that your level of happiness has almost *nothing* to do with how old you are, whether you are male or female, where you were born, what race you are, your educational level, or the status of your parents. [2]

One of the most important things any person can learn is that no one and nothing outside of yourself will bring you happiness. No one is coming to rescue you. Even winning the lottery will not make you happy. If you want your life to be happier you have to do something different, *yourself*.

---

[2] Myers, David G. *The Pursuit of Happiness*. New York: Avon Books, 1992.

The Happiness Choice

For centuries people have been debating what determines our fate. Is it in our genes or in our upbringing? Although these both have a strong influence on us, what really determines how happy we will be are the choices we make.

Take the story of two brothers who are twins. One grows up to be an alcoholic bum. The other becomes an extremely successful businessman. When the alcoholic is asked why he became a drunk, he replies, "My father was a drunk." When the successful businessman is asked why he became successful, he says, "My father was a drunk." Same background. Same upbringing. Different choices.

Every moment of every day events happen, and we respond to them. As we saw with the twins, our response is critical. One twin responded to the situation by feeling hopeless and giving up. The other responded by saying, "I'm not going to let that happen to me," worked very hard, and became successful.

You may not have control over what happens, but you have total control over how you choose to respond. Many times we fail to recognize that we are making a choice because of the speed with which the event and our reaction happen.

Imagine that you are walking down the street, and suddenly you see a big rattlesnake in front of you, poised to strike. Before you can think, you are getting the heck out of there. But it isn't *really* before you can think; it just happens so fast that it seems that way. The fact is that you've looked at a situation and made an intelligent decision about what to do according to how you see it. It goes like this: You see the snake. You make a decision—based on your background knowledge—that you're in a dangerous situation. You conclude that it's time to get out of danger and you are off and running, sometimes before you are even consciously aware that you *saw* the snake.

This is all good and fine when it comes to snakes. But there are many situations in life where our logic isn't so intelligent; rather, it is unthinking and habitual. We have created automatic habits of thinking and acting that are not in our best interest.

The first step to increasing your happiness is to realize that you *are* making choices. In every waking moment you are making a choice about how you will respond to a given situation, even when you are not fully aware that you are doing so. That choice will either increase your happiness or decrease your happiness. By recognizing and accepting this, you gain power over your responses. When you don't take responsibility for your choices and their consequences, it may feel easier in the short run. But over time you wind up feeling like a helpless victim, unable to make a difference in your own life, and this feeling leads to depression.

You will always have many automatic and habitual responses, and these are important. You wouldn't want to stop and ponder what to do when someone cuts in front of you in traffic, or debate the value of brushing your teeth every morning. That's why it is important to create specific behavioral habits that are proven to bring happiness.

So choosing the happiness habit means choosing to respond to life's events in ways that will bring you the long-term happiness you seek, rather than responding with automatic, unthinking actions that can undermine and even destroy your happiness.

The good news is there are certain traits and behaviors that consistently bring happiness and we can learn them. In his book, *The Pursuit of Happiness*, David Myers identifies the following four traits among people who consider themselves "extremely happy." Happy people:

+ Have a strong sense of personal control over their lives.

+ Are optimistic.

+ Like themselves.

+ Are outgoing.

In addition, happy people tend to believe in a purpose greater than themselves and do things that make a positive difference for others. They have close and intimate relationships. Happy people also handle adversity well.

Many of these traits can be developed through creating habits of "right thinking" and "right acting."

Right Thinking

Don't believe everything you think.

Many people confuse having thoughts with thinking. These are two entirely different things. Having thoughts is *passive*, while thinking is *active*. Thinking involves active choice. Thinking is critical to our happiness. In a single day 50,000 thoughts pass through the human mind. That's more than 34 thoughts every minute. Although most of these thoughts are unconscious, they do have an effect on us because we take action based on them. However, our thoughts come so fast that it seems like that's simply the way life is. We don't have an experience of actively choosing anything.

To be happy, we must have an awareness of the choices we are making, thereby gaining control over how we respond to our thoughts instead of reacting automatically to whatever pops into our head.

Without realizing it, most of us tend to focus on the negative, often seeing other people's behavior as having negative intent, and worrying about bad things that have happened or might happen. This kind of thinking consumes, paralyzes, and misdirects us. It creates unhappiness. This is not "right thinking."

Unhappiness can be lethal. It is when people are unhappy that they do bad things. When people are depressed they don't have the energy required to solve problems. Unhappy people are reactive and make poor choices. Without realizing it, many people have developed wrong thinking, or the "unhappiness habit."

The goal of right thinking is to focus on positive and productive thoughts. Right thinking doesn't mean you ignore your problems; it simply means that you handle them instead of dwelling on them. Avoiding problems leads to depression and hopelessness. Focusing on solutions gives us hope as well as direction and motivation.

People who intentionally focus on positive outcomes instead of negative ones are more successful, creative, productive, and loving. They are lifelong learners. They see adversity as a challenge and solve problems more easily. They have more fun and laughter. They achieve more of their goals, are healthier, and have less conflict in their lives.

There will always be difficulties in life. There will always be negative people. How we choose to let them affect us is what this program is about. Let's take a look at how Barbara used right thinking to handle a difficult situation in her life.

> *About three months ago I was planning on leaving my job. Escaping would probably be more like it. Some of the people I worked with were so negative and critical. When I told my boss I was offered another job, he counteroffered with such a large raise and other benefits that, after considering my options, I decided to stay for the next assignment. I'm in a freelance business, and for that amount of money I felt I could "grin and*

bear it" for a few more months. Besides, I'd always wanted to know how it would feel to "laugh all the way to the bank."

I soon realized I had made the wrong decision. Every morning as I walked from my car to my office I was miserable with anticipation and dread, thinking of the people I had to put up with. It made me feel crazy! And to think I believed the money would make up for the misery I faced.

Then I began to use the principles taught in CHOOSE THE HAPPINESS HABIT. I immediately realized that I was focusing all my attention on people I didn't like at work instead of the ones that I did like!

I decided to change my focus. As I walked to my office each morning I consciously disciplined myself to think about the co-workers I thought were terrific. I focused on how much I liked these people and how I hoped we would work together on many occasions during our careers. What a difference! I actually began to look forward to going to work!

The change in my attitude snowballed and began to affect the people around me. They started being more cheerful and fun to be around. It was hard for me to believe that such a simple action—taking control of my thoughts as I walked to my job—could make such a huge difference in my life.

This change has also affected my relationship with my husband. He used to have to suffer through my *complaints every night. Now we spend our time doing much more enjoyable things. I started this as a game. I see instead that I have learned a skill that will affect me all my life. I know now that it's not what happens to me that determines the quality of my life, it's how I respond to what happens to me. I know now that I have control over my responses.*

Sometimes forcing youself to do right thinking can feel like you're wrestling with a bear, but it is a worthwhile battle. And it is *always* possible, in every circumstance, to choose how you will react to what's happening. You don't believe me? Listen to Viktor Frankl, a Jewish psychiatrist who was in a concentration camp during World War II, which were some of the worst conditions human beings have ever suffered through. But even here, he discovered something remarkable:

We who lived in concentration camps can remember the men who walked through the huts comforting others, giving away their last piece of bread. They may have been few in number, but they offer sufficient proof that everything can be taken from a person but one thing: the last of the human freedoms—to choose one's attitude in any given set of circumstances, to choose one's own way.

Can you believe that? People were cold, miserable, and starving, yet they chose to spend their lives comforting others, giving away food! I doubt that they considered themselves happy. But they were probably at peace with themselves. They knew they had a choice about what their life was to be about. This is the best possible news. It means that you can change your world, your attitude, your mood, and even your actions by how you choose to respond to an event. By changing your focus or your thoughts, you can change your life. Now that's power.

Right Acting

Always do right. This will gratify some people and astonish the rest.
— Mark Twain

I have a support buddy. We talk every morning to support each other in keeping our commitments. I can tell the minute she says hello whether she has kept her commitments or not. If she sounds groggy and has no energy, I know she did not keep her promises. If she is cheerful, has a sparkle in her voice, and sounds on top of the world, I know she has done what she said she would.

"Right acting" is doing what *you* know to be the right thing. When you do that, you feel so good about yourself that you don't need drugs, shopping, television, food, or alcohol to feel good. You will be high in the best way possible—high on life and high on yourself.

Right acting takes into account your best interest, along with what is best for others, and the future.

Doing the right thing is beautifully described by John Wooden, a UCLA basketball coach who holds the world's record for the longest winning streak in any major sport

—88 games over four seasons. Some think his spectacular record will never be broken.

What did the wizard of Westwood do to bring out the best of his team? Did he say, "Go out and win one for the gipper?" Nope. In fact, he didn't talk about winning at all. Here are some of his inspiring words: [3]

> *To me success isn't outscoring someone, it's the peace of mind that comes from self-satisfaction in knowing you did your best. That's something each individual must determine for themselves. You can fool others, but you can't fool yourself.*
>
> *When it's over, I want your head up. And there's only one way your head can be up—and that's for you to know, not me, that you gave the best effort of which you're capable. If you do that, then the score doesn't really matter.*

Right acting is not always easy and certainly is not always agreed upon by everyone. One thing we know for certain is that we *will* make mistakes in life and we will fall short of our goals. That's why self-acceptance and forgiveness are a vital part of happiness. Sometimes it is hard to accept ourselves when we don't live up to our own expectations or when we do something we know is wrong.

We will never be perfect. Trying to be perfect stops us from taking action. It also stops us from learning the lessons from our errors that will help us to reach our goals.

---

[3] Aguayo, Rafael. *Dr. Deming.* New York: Fireside, 1991.

In fact, many times, it is through errors that we have our best discoveries.

We can learn a lesson about right acting from Babe Ruth. Babe is considered to be one of the world's greatest hitters, but he had to strike out 1,330 times before he won his title. His success was based on his willingness to take the risk of failure, learn from it, and step up to bat again. It's said that, "If you're not making mistakes, then you're not taking enough risks." To be a successful risk-taker, you must be able to accept that you won't be perfect at everything, forgive yourself, and jump back in the game when you fall short or have a disappointment.

So right acting is doing those things that will make you hold your head high. It is taking on challenges, facing problems, and taking risks. It is also knowing that, although life may not be a series of home runs, the way to get it over the fence is to keep stepping up to bat.

It is said that the quality of life is determined by what you do in the space between stimulus and response—choose the response that will bring happiness.

Make Happiness Your #1 Priority

Now you know what happiness is, why it is important, and where to find it. Your next step is to make happiness a habit.

First, you have to recognize that your happiness is the most important thing in the world. There is no greater contribution you can make to the world than to become a person who consistently experiences joy and enthusiasm for life.

The best way for you to have happy loved ones, children, and co-workers is for you to be happy. They will follow your lead. No matter what you say, if you are stopped by adversity, they probably will be too. If you take setbacks in stride and get right back on track you provide a model for them to follow.

Following the HabitBuilder will help motivate you to success but it will not take the place of your personal commitment.

As we said earlier, building new habits to replace negative entrenched habits will take discipline and time. You can begin your happiness habit right now by saying, "I choose to live a happy life."

The HabitBuilder

The HabitBuilder is a systematic program designed to help you achieve happiness, regardless of your life's circumstances. Using the HabitBuilder will make you aware of the happiness you already have and will focus you on the positive aspects of your life's journey.

The three critical abilities necessary for you to achieve happiness are (1) appreciating what you already have, (2) continual personal growth, and (3) being able to respond effectively to adverse situations. Your ability to be in control of these will determine your level of happiness.

Colette, a famous French writer, once said, "I've really had a wonderful life. I only wish I had realized it sooner."

The most effective way to recognize the good in your life is to write it down in the first section of the Habit-Builder, in your daily moments of happiness. Moments of happiness are different from affirmations. An affirmation is a statement of belief in something that may or may not actually be in your life at the present time. The purpose of the daily moments of happiness process is to capture on paper the good that is in your life right now.

It's important to write your daily moments of happiness. Writing down the positive is an acknowledgment of your reality. You are the only one who can determine what is good in your life. Awareness of your good will begin to alter your outlook. This, in turn, will give you power and energy to handle problems more easily and effectively.

The second critical ability is continuing to grow as a person. To achieve this, you will be working on one of the habits of happy people each day and expanding your ability in this area. The third ability to develop is learning how to recognize, face, and resolve problems. We all have misfortunes in our lives. Dwelling or fixating on them prevents us from taking effective action. The tools in the second section of the HabitBuilder will make you more effective and powerful in dealing with adverse situations.

In his book, *Learned Optimism,* Martin Seligman talks about his landmark psychological study revealing a phenomenon he termed "learned helplessness." Seligman discovered that people actually learn to become helpless. This learned helplessness affects how they approach situations in their lives and how their approach affects the outcome of the situation. People who have learned helplessness find themselves in situations where they perceive they have no control. This perception leads them to feel helpless and dejected. They believe it would be useless to try, so they don't. The next time they are in similar circumstances, they continue to feed their belief in their own helplessness by once again giving up hope. They have set up a circle of helplessness. Their behavior becomes a habit that is soon entrenched in their lives.

It is important to note that while we are living this process of learned helplessness, we don't think of ourselves as helpless, but rather that "this is reality." We believe that we are making rational and intelligent choices given the circumstances we're in. That point of view is what needs to be broken up. It is tunnel vision that gives us little opportunity to affect our lives.

Several years ago I owned a bakery. I was approached by a local business owner who offered me a contract to prepare and deliver specialty foods to his restaurant. He provided me with recipes for all of the foods except the muffins. The muffin recipe was mine to create.

I worked very hard to develop the perfect muffin. I tried recipe after recipe but none seemed to work well. Finally, I had to make my first delivery. I crossed my fingers and prayed as the muffins baked. The salads and the specialty dishes all came out great. But the muffins looked more like large bread crumbs than muffins. I was very embarrassed. I dreaded making the delivery, certain that I would lose the contract.

As I showed the businessman my muffins I said, "Well, I guess you won't want me to do this anymore." He looked at me with surprise and said, "You sure give up easily. Go back and try again." I did exactly that and eventually I created a suitable recipe.

The point to my story is that I approached the situation with a pessimistic view, and I didn't recognize that it was my point of view, not reality. The facts seemed clear to me then: You get one chance, and if you blow it that's the end. Since I had "blown it," it never even occurred to me that I had another possible chance.

Using the tools in the HabitBuilder will help you develop new ways of thinking and the power to solve problems. For what is important is not that you solve a particular problem, but that you realize you have the power to solve your problems.

How the HabitBuilder Works

The HabitBuilder is a 90-day program designed to get rid of negative, entrenched thinking habits and replace them with productive ones. This is done only through consistent, repetitive practice. It's important that you follow the HabitBuilder as a daily program. Daily practice is a series of small steps that lead to success. You are looking for small changes: they are more effective and longer-lasting than one large change. If you miss a day or more, simply begin where you left off and continue until you have finished the full 90 days. Remember that it's better to start, stop, and then start again, than never to start at all!

The HabitBuilder Workbook Overview

Daily Moments of Happiness

The daily moments of happiness section is divided into two tasks. Here you will begin to create your focus. You will keep a daily record of happy moments, and each day for 13 weeks you will practice one of the 13 habits or characteristics of happy people.[4] The reason the program is 13 weeks is because that's how long it takes to change your thought patterns. It is critical that you continue the program for the full time period, even if you are experiencing immediate results. The purpose of the program is to have the desired thought patterns become habit, and that can only happen through repetition.

If you use your daily moments of happiness page faithfully, you will see a change within the first week of using the HabitBuilder program.

The HabitBuilder Tool Chest

To achieve a happy state of being, one must be able to resolve problems in a manner that is both effective and appropriate. By using this part of the program on your problems over the next 90 days, you will become more skilled at solving problems. What is important is that you discover your ability to handle adversity, no matter what the situation. This section has three tools designed to help you develop this skill. They are:

1. **The Happiness Treasure Chest:** This tool will help you remember the happy things in your life. Used frequently, you will find power to reduce negative thinking.

---

[4] See the appendix for an explanation of where these habits came from and why they are important.

2. ***Find the Pearl:*** Every adverse situation has at least one positive element. This tool will help you change your focus and look for the "pearl" in your situation.

3. ***The Personal Power Page:*** This problem-solving tool will help problem resolution. To use it effectively, however, you must focus on core issues. This means you may have to let go of some of the emotional stuff that always accompanies problems. Many times objectivity about your situation is necessary before you can see a solution. Follow the five steps as outlined and call a trusted friend if you get stuck.

The HabitBuilder Workbook Overview Summary

Daily Moments of Happiness

PURPOSE: To make you aware of and bring more happiness into your life by changing your focus.

WHEN TO USE: Every day.

HOW TO USE: Write down three things that make you happy every single day. Two are of your choosing. The third relates to a specific characteristic proven to bring happiness.

The HabitBuilder Tool Chest

PURPOSE: To give you tools to effectively solve your problems, and reduce the amount of time spent on problems.

WHEN TO USE: Whenever you have a problem and (1) find yourself stopping; (2) feel down, depressed, or hopeless; or (3) want a lift.

HOW TO USE: Look over the three tools and use whichever one seems appropriate. You may want to use all three on a problem.

SECTION 1

Daily Moments of Happiness

A 90-Day Workout

This is the heart and soul of building the happiness habit. Every day, for the next 90 days, your task is to write down at least two moments of happiness. The reason the program is 90 days long is because research has proven that it takes at least 90 days to change your thought patterns. It is critical that you continue the program for the full time period even if you are getting immediate results. The purpose is to make sure the new ways of thinking take hold and become habit.

Each day has three spaces for writing. In the first two spaces write down anything that makes you happy. The third space is organized around 13 habits that are personality traits and characteristic of happy people. Each week, for 13 weeks, you will be practicing and developing one of the 13 characteristics that has been proven to increase people's happiness.

A moment of happiness can be any incident or event that you feel good about. It may be something that makes you smile, brings a warm feeling, makes you feel good about yourself, or makes you laugh out loud. It could be a moment of inspiration, a personal victory, or special time with a loved one. It might be one or two words, such as "my grandson," or it might be an entire paragraph describing an event, such as how you handled yourself in a certain situation. Don't worry about your spelling or writing. Concentrate instead on a good description of the moment. Writing in vivid detail often brings a special moment truly alive.

You may also want to take time to look back at the previous days' events and think about the chain of happy moments you are creating.

1

Happy People Like Themselves

*When you let your light shine through, you
give other people permission to do the same.*

– Marianne Williamson

There are two keys to liking yourself. The first is to do
the things that will make you like yourself. People whose
actions are consistent with what they believe to be the
right thing feel good about themselves. They don't need
to chase other people's approval because they the have
approval of the most important person in the world:
themselves. When people do what it takes to "walk their
talk," they have a freedom and spontaneity that is not
available any other way.

The second key to liking yourself is to identify those
things that you like about yourself. When I am teaching
my classes, I frequently have people give feedback on
themselves before other people comment. I always ask
them to tell me what went well or what they liked before
I ask them where they might improve. The most frequent
answer is, "Nothing went well," or they skip that part and
tell me everything they did wrong. Sometimes it's like
pulling teeth to get people to acknowledge themselves.

Yet it is critical because if we don't love and appreciate ourselves there is little likelihood that we can truly appreciate others. As Opray Winfrey said, "True love begins with yourself."

Assignment for This Week

Throughout this 90-day workout, each day you will describe at least two moments of happiness you had. This week, you will also write down at least one thing you like about yourself or something you are proud of. If you want to shout it from the rooftop, do that too!

The world has rarely treated happiness as a state worthy of serious respect. And yet, if we see someone who, in spite of life's adversities, is happy a good deal of the time, we should recognize that we are looking at a spiritual achievement — and one worth aspiring to.

— Nathaniel Branden

1

Daily Moments of Happiness

Day _____ Date _____

In the space below, describe at least two moments of happiness you had today.

1. _____

_____

_____

_____

_____

_____

_____

2. _____

_____

_____

_____

_____

_____

_____

Habit #1: **Happy people like themselves**

Assignment: What do I like about myself?

_____

_____

_____

_____

_____

_____

_____

_____

Accepting yourself and living in the moment will together increase your opportunities for experiencing true joy. When you have feelings of true joy on a regular basis, you are moving toward self-love. And that is a beautiful experience.

– Bob Greene, *A Journal of Daily Renewal*

1

Daily Moments of Happiness

Day _____ Date _____

In the space below, describe at least two moments of happiness you had today.

1. _____

_____

_____

_____

_____

_____

_____

2. _____

_____

_____

_____

_____

_____

_____

Habit #1: **Happy people like themselves**

Assignment: What do I like about myself?

_____

_____

_____

_____

_____

_____

_____

_____

_____

_____

Make one person happy each day, even if it's yourself.

– Author unknown

1

Daily Moments of Happiness

Day _____ Date _____

In the space below, describe at least two moments of happiness you had today.

1. _____

_____

_____

_____

_____

_____

_____

2. _____

_____

_____

_____

_____

_____

_____

Habit #1: **Happy people like themselves**

Assignment: What do I like about myself?

_____

_____

_____

_____

_____

_____

_____

_____

_____

Regardless of who you are or what you do, remember that nothing is more important than your own sense of happiness and inner peace, and that of your loved ones.

– Richard Carlson, Ph.D.

1

Daily Moments of Happiness

Day _____ Date _____

In the space below, describe at least two moments of happiness you had today.

1. _____

_____

_____

_____

_____

_____

2. _____

_____

_____

_____

_____

_____

Habit #1: **Happy people like themselves**

Assignment: What do I like about myself?

_____

_____

_____

_____

_____

_____

_____

_____

_____

_____

_____

*The summit of happiness
is reached when a person
is ready to be what he is.*

– Erasmus

1

Daily Moments of Happiness

Day _____ Date _____

In the space below, describe at least two moments of
happiness you had today.

1. _____

_____

_____

_____

_____

_____

_____

2. _____

_____

_____

_____

_____

_____

_____

Habit #1: **Happy people like themselves**

Assignment: What do I like about myself?

_____

_____

_____

_____

_____

_____

_____

_____

When we laugh, we open a space within that makes room to love ourselves, to welcome ourselves into our own hearts, to love as much as we can from wherever we are, and to forgive the sweet human flaws that make us so divinely comical.

– Nicky Marone, Women and Risk

1

Daily Moments of Happiness

Day _____ Date _____

In the space below, describe at least two moments of happiness you had today.

1. _____

_____

_____

_____

_____

_____

2. _____

_____

_____

_____

_____

_____

Habit #1: **Happy people like themselves**

Assignment: What do I like about myself?

_____

_____

_____

_____

_____

_____

_____

It's not helpful to condemn our present behavior patterns . . . There is no need to fight old habits. Start new ones. It is resisting an old habit that puts you in the trench. Starting a new pattern is easy when done with childlike regard for imagined difficulties. You can prove this to yourself by your own experience.

– Tim Gallwey, *The Inner Game of Tennis*

1

Daily Moments of Happiness

Day _____ Date _____

In the space below, describe at least two moments of happiness you had today.

1. _____

_____

_____

_____

_____

_____

_____

2. _____

_____

_____

_____

_____

_____

_____

Habit #1: **Happy people like themselves**

Assignment: What do I like about myself?

_____

_____

_____

_____

_____

_____

_____

_____

_____

_____

_____

*You have brains in your
head and feet in your shoes,
you can steer yourself in
any direction you choose.*

– Dr. Seuss

2

Happy People Are Optimistic

Perpetual optimism is a force multiplier.

– Colin Powell

People who are optimistic achieve more of their goals and are healthier, not to mention a lot more fun to be around.

Being optimistic does not mean that you pretend that everything is okay when it's not. It means that you expect the best possible outcome. You focus on the most hopeful parts of a situation. On the other hand, a pessimist expects a negative outcome and feels helpless to do anything to change the situation. The following story shows the difference between optimism and pessimism.

John and Jerry are part of a swimming team. In one practice session they both fall short of their goal time. John says to himself, "Oh no! I'd better work harder next time." He works harder and goes on to win Olympic gold medals for swimming. Jerry says to himself, "Oh no! I'm not as good as I thought. I guess I don't belong on this team," and he gives up on the race.

This is a true story. What's most revealing is that the young men actually did reach their goal time. They were given a false time to determine how they would react to failure. What made the difference was each swimmer's reaction to a perceived failure. One saw it as a call to action, the other saw it as a reason to give up.

In his book, *Emotional Intelligence*, Daniel Goleman explains, "People who are optimistic see a failure as due to something that can be changed, so they can succeed next time around, while pessimists take the blame for failure, ascribing it to some lasting characteristic they are helpless to change."

What's not so obvious is that probably neither of them realized they were "seeing" the situation at all. The critical element of learning to think and act optimistically is to recognize when you are viewing an event in a particular way, or "reacting." When you identify that you are having a reaction, you have the power to choose the most effective response.

Assignment for This Week

Each day write down an event where you recognize that your perception affected your actions and the outcome. This can be anything from how you see a traffic jam, failure to achieve a goal, or how you walk into the house at the end of your workday.

2

Daily Moments of Happiness

Day _____   Date _____

In the space below, describe at least two moments of
happiness you had today.

1. _____

   _____

   _____

   _____

   _____

   _____

   _____

2. _____

   _____

   _____

   _____

   _____

   _____

   _____

Habit #2: **Happy people are optimistic**

Assignment: How did my point of view determine the
effect an event had on me? What did I do? What was the
result?

_____

_____

_____

_____

_____

_____

_____

_____

_____

_____

_No pessimist ever discovered the secrets of
the stars, or sailed to an uncharted land, or
opened a new heaven to the human spirit._

— Helen Keller

2

Daily Moments of Happiness

Day _____ Date _____

In the space below, describe at least two moments of happiness you had today.

1. _____

_____

_____

_____

_____

_____

2. _____

_____

_____

_____

_____

_____

Habit #2: **Happy people are optimistic**

Assignment: How did my point of view determine the effect an event had on me? What did I do? What was the result?

_____

_____

_____

_____

_____

_____

_____

When we see that whatever we believe becomes manifest in our lives, we might as well believe the very best. We learn to believe the best of ourselves and of others, not out of blindness to faults, but out of well-founded hope in creating the most positive self-fulfilling prophecies.

– Dr. Richard Gillett,
Change Your Mind, Change Your World

2

Daily Moments of Happiness

Day _____ Date _____

In the space below, describe at least two moments of happiness you had today.

1. _____

_____

_____

_____

_____

_____

_____

2. _____

_____

_____

_____

_____

_____

_____

Habit #2: **Happy people are optimistic**

Assignment: How did my point of view determine the effect an event had on me? What did I do? What was the result?

_____

_____

_____

_____

_____

_____

_____

_____

_____

_____

*An optimist may see a light where
there is none, but why must the
pessimist always run to blow it out?*

– Michel de Saint-Pierre

2

Daily Moments of Happiness

Day _____   Date _____

In the space below, describe at least two moments of
happiness you had today.

1. _____

   _____

   _____

   _____

   _____

   _____

   _____

2. _____

   _____

   _____

   _____

   _____

   _____

   _____

Habit #2: **Happy people are optimistic**

Assignment: How did my point of view determine the effect an event had on me? What did I do? What was the result?

_____

_____

_____

_____

_____

_____

_____

_____

_____

_____

_____

_____

Always know in your heart that you are far bigger than anything that can happen to you.

– Dan Zadra, *Little Miracles*

2

Daily Moments of Happiness

Day _____ Date _____

In the space below, describe at least two moments of
happiness you had today.

1. _____

   _____

   _____

   _____

   _____

   _____

   _____

2. _____

   _____

   _____

   _____

   _____

   _____

   _____

Habit #2: **Happy people are optimistic**

Assignment: How did my point of view determine the effect an event had on me? What did I do? What was the result?

_____

_____

_____

_____

_____

_____

_____

_____

_____

_____

In the long run, the pessimist may be proved right, but the optimist has a better time on the trip.

– Author unknown

2

Daily Moments of Happiness

Day _____ Date _____

In the space below, describe at least two moments of happiness you had today.

1. _____

_____

_____

_____

_____

_____

2. _____

_____

_____

_____

_____

_____

Habit #2: **Happy people are optimistic**

Assignment: How did my point of view determine the effect an event had on me? What did I do? What was the result?

_____

_____

_____

_____

_____

_____

_____

_____

_____

_____

No person ever injured their eyesight by looking on the bright side of things.

– Author unknown

2

Daily Moments of Happiness

Day _____   Date _____

In the space below, describe at least two moments of happiness you had today.

1. _____

_____

_____

_____

_____

_____

_____

2. _____

_____

_____

_____

_____

_____

_____

Habit #2: **Happy people are optimistic**

Assignment: How did my point of view determine the effect an event had on me? What did I do? What was the result?

_____

_____

_____

_____

_____

_____

_____

_____

_____

Optimism is an intellectual choice.
– Diana Schneider

Dear Happiness HabitBuilder,

Congratulations on making it through the first two weeks! This week you will be taking on the area of being in control of your life, the most essential trait for being happy. This makes sense, because if you're in control and you don't like something, you have the power to change it!

Because this trait has such a strong effect on your happiness, and is so complex, this explanation is quite a bit longer than the others. By reading this section and doing the exercises this week, you will find new areas of control and enjoy doing it.

I wish you much joy in discovering this power for yourself.

Love, Pam

3

Happy People Believe They Are in Control of Their Lives

Can't nothing make your life
work if you ain't the architect.

– Terry McMillan

What is the best way to increase your happiness? The most effective way to increase your happiness is to take greater control of your life. People who feel that they are in charge of their destiny are happier, healthier, and more productive than any other group of people.

What being in control means is that you are the one who influences your life—not outside events, other people, your feelings, or the circumstance of the moment. It means that you determine what happens to you through your own efforts.

If you view outside forces as determining your life, you will be more defensive and reactive. If you view your life as the result of your own actions, you will be more proactive and accomplish more of your goals.

However, what you can control and what you can't is not always easy to identify. There is a famous prayer attributed to Friedrich Oetinger and Reinhold Niebuhr called "The Serenity Prayer." It says, "God grant me the serenity to accept the things I cannot change, the courage to change the things I can, and the wisdom to know the difference."

It's knowing the difference that has been one of humanity's greatest challenges. Over and over we discover that we *can* control or change things we never thought possible. Yet, at times we also try to change things that we cannot control, which can lead to frustration and depression. Although some believe that persistence is what makes the difference in life, others define insanity as "doing the same thing over and over again and expecting a different result." Trying to decide which is which could make your eyes spin around in your head.

Yet, if we want to expand our boundaries and gain greater control, it is important to understand what we can't control, what we can control, and what is important to control.

What We CAN'T Control

We all pretty much agree that we can't change the weather. That seems easy. But my husband just reminded me that in the last 50 years, science has learned how to seed clouds to create rain. So I guess we *can* change some weather, and we will probably control it even more often as time goes on. But for now, *most* of the time we can't change the weather.

Well, we certainly can't change the past. But we can change our interpretation of the past. For instance, some people see a tragic childhood as undermining their hope of a successful life. Others see a difficult childhood as giving them the motivation to succeed. So, in a way we *can* change the past—or at least how the past influences us today.

There are certain physical things we can't change. But wait. Everyone believed it was physically impossible to run a four-minute mile. Never in recorded history had anyone ever broken the four-minute mile. Articles were written explaining that the human body was constructed in a way that made it impossible to run that fast. Then, on May 6, 1954, Roger Bannister ran a mile in less than four minutes.

What's most fascinating about this is what happened next. Shortly after Bannister broke the four-minute mile a second person did it. Within months, many others also did so. Now runners regularly break the four-minute mile. Did human physiology change? No. What changed was people's point of view—from "I can't do it" to "I can do it." What had been thought impossible for 2,500 years "became possible" in an instant (well actually, just under four minutes).

What you can't control can be pretty difficult to determine. Yet there are definitely some things beyond our control. I can't fly to the moon this afternoon, lose 50 pounds in a day, or build well-toned, strong muscles in a week. However, what is uncontrollable is open to question, and what might be out of reach for someone else may indeed be within your grasp. So I will leave it up to you to determine for yourself what you can't control, and let's turn our attention to what we *can* control, and what is important to control.

What We CAN Control

We can control how we think, what we say, our interpretations, and what we do. In short, we can control ourselves. And by controlling ourselves we can influence what happens and to some degree what other people do.

We Can Control Our Thoughts

Controlling our thoughts can determine the outcome of a situation. I was reminded of this one day while I was jogging. I was going on an ambitious six-mile run. I scoped out the territory and was jogging along when I started feeling an overwhelming urge to stop running. "You've done enough. It's okay to stop now," the voice inside my head shouted.

I hadn't been running very long and I knew that I was physically okay. Then it dawned on me. Those negative thoughts and feelings began when I started running uphill —when the going got tough.

I had promised myself that I would not stop, and that I would jog—even if it was very slowly—for the entire distance. But my negative thoughts weren't going away and I was only on mile two of the six miles. It did not look good. I was just about to stop when a picture of myself jumping up and down for joy, victorious at my front door, flashed through my mind. And that's what carried me through. After that, whenever I made that run and felt like giving up, I took control of my thoughts and focused on the picture of me gloriously happy after successfully reaching my goal. That motivated me to finish.

Although you can't control many of the thoughts that pop into your head, you *can* control how long they stay there and how you respond to them. And, with practice, over time you actually can change your thought patterns. If you have a habit of focusing on the negative, with practice you can change that habit. Taking control of how you respond to your thoughts, and what thoughts you focus on, can make the difference between success and failure, happiness and unhappiness.

We Can Control Our Interpretation

You see an old friend on the street and go to say hello, but he avoids you, quickly walking the other way. Your boss calls you and says, "I want to see you immediately." Your spouse brings you flowers.

In each case, you feel something is not right. Your friend must be mad at you. You must have messed up at work. Your spouse must be feeling guilty about something.

But is that really the way it is? Or did you look at the facts—your friend walked away, your boss wants to see you, your spouse brought you flowers—and then add an interpretation on top of that? (My friend is mad at me, my boss is upset, my spouse did something wrong.)

Your interpretation of the facts happens at lightning speed, so fast that it frequently gets confused with facts.

This is critical, because your interpretation can dictate what happens next. The facts are the facts, but your interpretation of the facts may be completely wrong. Your boss may be extremely pleased with your work, or have some organizational news to convey. Your spouse may be feeling especially loving, and bought you flowers to show it. Your friend may not have seen you, or may have been late for an appointment. But you felt insulted by his "snub," and cut off the relationship with that friend, thus making your erroneous interpretation come true.

A dramatic example of the power of interpretation is the true story of a man who was accidentally trapped inside a train. He was in a refrigeration unit, and he knew that if he didn't get out soon he would freeze to death. He scratched that message on a box inside the train car. After being trapped for five hours, he was discovered dead. But it turned out that the refrigeration unit was broken and it never got below 60 degrees. He would have been just fine if he had distracted his thoughts and waited to be rescued. What killed him was his interpretation and his thoughts. (People could tell this by reading what he wrote on the box.) The fact was that it wasn't cold. But the conclusion he drew, based on his thoughts, was that it was freezing and he would die. Which is exactly what happened.

Where do these interpretations come from? They come from past experiences which may not be accurate now. *This is crucial*, because what you see (your interpretation) can dictate your actions. And *what was true in a different time and place may not be relevant in this situation*.

Although you will always have automatic interpretations, you are not stuck with them. You have no control over the facts, but you do have control over your interpretation of them and how you respond to them. You can interpret a conflict as a break in a relationship or as an opportunity to get closer together. You can interpret a misdeed of your child as confirmation that she is troublesome or as a wake-up call to teach values and spend time together.

You have total control over your interpretation. Perhaps not the instant it happens, but after a brief reflection, you have the power to choose the interpretation that will create the most positive and beneficial result.

We Can Control Our Behavior

Although controlling your thoughts and interpretations can dramatically affect what you do, controlling your behavior is also key to taking charge of your life. At one time it was believed that you had to change your thoughts before you could change your behavior. But that has proven to be untrue. Sometimes it's more effective to *act* your way into a new thought pattern than to *think* your way into new behaviors. In fact, sometimes it's the only way. No matter how much you *think* you are good at using a computer, it will make no difference until you sit in front of one and actually learn how to use it.

Gaining control over your behavior may start by simply taking action—no matter what you think or feel about something. Instead of waiting for the right time, or for the fear or feeling of helplessness to go away, *just doing it* can be the critical key to gaining mastery of your life.

Can We Control Other People?

You may not be able to control other people, but what you say and do certainly has an influence on them. Below are some examples of how people took control of their own behavior and the dramatic effect it had on the people around them.

In his book, *Success Is a Choice*, basketball coach Rick Pitino tells how he used to berate his team when they did poorly. One day he realized that they weren't improving, and that scolding them reduced their morale and their performance got even worse.

Realizing the impact of his negative approach, Rick changed his focus to the positive, encouraging the players to feel good about themselves and believe they would win. When the players' attitudes changed, they began winning.

Joan was the manager of the Los Angeles office of a nationwide computer company. Her branch was ranked the lowest of 23 offices nationwide. She decided to really go for it and make it the best. When she announced her goal at the national company sales meeting, the president of the company sarcastically snapped at her, "You can't change people, and your people aren't good enough!" in front of all the other managers. After a moment's hesitation, she replied, "You're right. But I can change myself. And if I change, maybe they will change."

And that's exactly what happened. Joan made all sorts of changes in herself. She learned what she needed to do to provide her staff with the support and motivation they needed to accomplish her goal. Her staff responded. By the end of the next quarter, her branch had moved up dramatically, and by the end of the year her branch was not only #1, it was way ahead of the branch in second place.

I know of a mother who complained bitterly that her children wouldn't do the dishes as they had promised. She was always stuck with a dirty kitchen to clean up before cooking dinner. Self-esteem expert Nathaniel Branden advised her to stop cooking. The deal she had made with her sons was that they would wash the dishes and take out the trash, and she would cook. If they didn't keep their end of the bargain, she shouldn't keep her end. It certainly undermined the agreement when she did their work.

One night she sat down and read a book instead of cooking. Surprised that she wasn't cooking, the children asked when dinner would be ready. She replied simply, "I don't cook in a dirty kitchen." The place was cleaned in record time and they soon sat down to a wonderful meal. The next night, the same situation—a little testing going on. She enjoyed her book for a few minutes and then the kitchen was clean.

The real turning point came a couple of weeks later. The boys had been diligent but slipped, and Mom walked into a dirty kitchen. Although she was tempted to help them out (after all, they had been so good), she held firm

73

and enjoyed her book for a few minutes. The kids swung into action right away. The lesson had been learned, and now her children don't "forget" any more.

In one famous study, grade school teachers were told that certain children were very intelligent and would perform excellently in their class that year. And sure enough, those children's work was outstanding. They did so well, in fact, that by the end of the year the children's IQs had actually gone up. But the truth was that these children had been chosen at random, and they weren't "stars" until they were treated like stars.

In each of the above cases people changed, sometimes dramatically. They started winning games, they became more productive, because of how they were treated, not because someone tried to change them. Although you may not be able to control the outcome, you often have enormous power to influence people through the way you conduct yourself, the example you set, and the way you treat people.

There are some people who will do extremely well or poorly no matter how you treat them. In the story about Joan and her mission to be #1, Joan had five salespeople working for her. Two of them were doing so poorly that they were given a deadline for improving or they would need to find work elsewhere. One of those salespeople became one of the five best in the nation and the other found work elsewhere. So you may not experience 100% success with everyone, but if you start by looking to see what is contributing to the problem and what you can do to impact it, you will be in a much more powerful position to affect your destiny than if you just complain about what's wrong. The key to changing other people is to change yourself.

What Is Important to Control

As we have seen, we can control our thoughts, interpretations, and behaviors. But the first thing to take charge of is our overall point of view about life, for this dramatically affects our thoughts and behaviors.

People usually look at the world from one of two basic points of view. One way is, "Outside events are in charge of my life." The other is, "I am in charge of my life."

When people believe that external forces determine their fate, they experience very little control over what happens to them. Because they feel that what they do will not make much difference, it is difficult for them to get moving, take risks, or put in the effort required to accomplish their goals and dreams.

When people believe they are in charge of their lives, and that what they do determines their results, they are more highly motivated. When things don't go well, they are willing to put in the extra effort required for success. Because they are confident that they will get the goodies if they do the work, they are willing to take the risks and initiative to make things happen.

So which perspective is correct? The answer is neither. You can make an ironclad case for each side. What's really important is not which way of thinking is correct, but which is most beneficial. This is illustrated by Virginia Wade, a famous tennis player who changed from a "they're-in-control" point of view to an "I'm-in-control" perspective.

Virginia had been in the finals at Wimbledon every year for 15 years and had lost every single year. Winning the big one looked hopeless. Then one day she made a personal commitment to win at Wimbledon, declaring, "This is the year I'm going to win." By setting that goal she put herself in charge. She then saw all kinds of things she needed to do that she had never realized before when she had been drifting along. She got herself a coach and worked passionately and relentlessly the entire next year, learning what she needed to do to win at Wimbledon.

Standing proudly in the winner's circle, holding her medallion high over her head as tears of joy streamed down her face, she basked in the glory of her achievement as the crowd cheered wildly for ten minutes. Virginia Wade had achieved something she had not been able to do in 15 years, and never *would* have been able to do if she hadn't put herself in charge. That is the power of putting yourself in charge. And it can be done at any point in your life.

What's so fantastic is that it's really very simple to start. Taking control means setting a goal and taking the steps to make it happen. Many of those steps are revealed the moment you set the goal. It does not have to be a newsworthy event like winning at Wimbledon or running a four-minute mile. It also doesn't mean creating a goal or a vision and then forcing or manipulating other people into following it. It means controlling yourself and operating in a manner consistent with your desires.

Laura's goal was to have a close, intimate, and sharing relationship with her husband. It troubled her that her husband wasn't very open with her. He never shared his innermost concerns or thoughts. She worked on figuring out if there was something she might be doing that contributed to his silence. In her search, one night she caught herself making a sarcastic put-down of him in front of friends. She suddenly realized that she wouldn't be open with someone if she was afraid they would put her down, and decided to stop making that kind of comment immediately. When she stopped making fun of him, her husband became more relaxed and open with her.

If Laura had believed she was helpless to do anything about the circumstances of her life and her husband's openness with her, she might have thought, He's not an open person, and succumbed to a life of loneliness. She also might have complained and criticized him for being uptight, which would have only made things worse.

Most people have certain areas of their lives where they feel they are in charge. But there are other areas where they don't feel so competent. I feel that I am very much an "I'm-in-charge" person. But when I started observing and listening to myself I was startled to see how often I didn't feel in control. I found myself unconsciously blaming other people and circumstances for problems.

Oddly enough, this realization was terrific news! It cleared up the mystery about why I felt depressed and hopeless at certain times.

One way to find out how you view the world is to listen to how you talk to other people or even to yourself. If you frequently hear yourself saying things like: "I couldn't help it," "They won't let me," "It's not my fault," "I was born that way," "It was meant to be," "If only..." "There's nothing I can do about it," "I just felt like it," "I have to," "That's just the way I am," "She makes me so mad," "I ought to, but..." "I should, but..." "I'd like to, but..." "I can't," or "I'm not good enough"—if you blame your problems on other people, circumstances, your feelings, your upbringing—or if you're feeling helpless or hopeless, you may be giving away control of your life without even realizing it.

The wonderful thing is that you can do something about it. Those nagging, underlying "victim" thoughts and feelings that stop you from taking control of your life can be changed.

Taking greater charge of your life may be a lot of work, but the rewards are outstanding. At Illinois Bell headquarters in Chicago, psychologist Salvatore Maddi gave a 15-week course that taught people how to take more control over their lives. At the end of the program their job satisfaction had doubled! In addition, their anxiety and depression had gone way down. They also had fewer headaches, less frequent insomnia, and their blood pressure went from an average of 130/82 down to 120/77.

When they were surveyed months later, the results had continued to get even better. So taking increasing control has a compound effect. Lest you think this might have happened anyway, a group of managers in the same company who did not take the course showed no such changes. Increasing your control over your universe will not only light up your life, it will make you healthier.

It may feel like it's easier to absolve yourself from responsibility for your life, but it is much more painful in the long run. You won't experience the joys of really living, the thrill of achievement, or the satisfaction of doing your personal best.

When you choose to see yourself in charge of your life, it is exhilarating. You can produce all kinds of results you never thought possible. You see opportunities for action you were blind to before. By choosing the happiness habit you have already started taking greater control of your life.

Assignment for This Week

Write down an instance each day where you chose to take charge of a situation over which you had previously thought you had no control, or you released an event you realized you couldn't control.

3

Daily Moments of Happiness

Day _____ Date _____

In the space below, describe at least two moments of happiness you had today.

1. _____

_____

_____

_____

_____

_____

_____

2. _____

_____

_____

_____

_____

_____

_____

Habit #3: **Happy people believe they are in control of their lives**

Assignment: How did I influence something I didn't think I had control over, or release something I couldn't control today?

_____

_____

_____

_____

_____

_____

_____

_____

_____

Always leave enough time in your life to do something that makes you happy, satisfied, even joyous. That has more of an effect on economic well-being than any other single factor.

– Paul Hawken

81

3

Daily Moments of Happiness

Day _____ Date _____

In the space below, describe at least two moments of happiness you had today.

1. _____

_____

_____

_____

_____

_____

_____

2. _____

_____

_____

_____

_____

_____

_____

Habit #3:   **Happy people believe they are in
             control of their lives**

Assignment: How did I influence something I didn't
think I had control over, or release something I couldn't
control today?

_____

_____

_____

_____

_____

_____

_____

_____

*While environment or genetic influ-
ences may be very powerful, they
do not control us. We're not victims.
We're not the product of our past.
We are the product of our choices.*

– Stephen Covey

3

Daily Moments of Happiness

Day _____ Date _____

In the space below, describe at least two moments of happiness you had today.

1. _____

_____

_____

_____

_____

_____

_____

2. _____

_____

_____

_____

_____

_____

_____

Habit #3: **Happy people believe they are in control of their lives**

Assignment: How did I influence something I didn't think I had control over, or release something I couldn't control today?

_____

_____

_____

_____

_____

_____

_____

_____

_____

In creating, the only
hard thing is to begin;
A grass blade's no easier
to make than an oak.

– James Russell Lowell

3

Daily Moments of Happiness

Day _____   Date _____

In the space below, describe at least two moments of happiness you had today.

1. _____

   _____

   _____

   _____

   _____

   _____

   _____

2. _____

   _____

   _____

   _____

   _____

   _____

   _____

Habit #3: **Happy people believe they are in control of their lives**

Assignment: How did I influence something I didn't think I had control over, or release something I couldn't control today?

_____

_____

_____

_____

_____

_____

_____

_____

_____

_____

*To say yes to life is one and the
same as saying yes to oneself.*

– Dag Hammarskjold

3

Daily Moments of Happiness

Day _____   Date _____

In the space below, describe at least two moments of happiness you had today.

1. _____

_____

_____

_____

_____

_____

2. _____

_____

_____

_____

_____

_____

Habit #3: **Happy people believe they are in control of their lives**

Assignment: How did I influence something I didn't think I had control over, or release something I couldn't control today?

_____

_____

_____

_____

_____

_____

_____

_____

I can choose to be happy now, or I can try to happy when . . . or if . . .

– Spencer Johnson, *The Precious Present*

3

Daily Moments of Happiness

Day _____   Date _____

In the space below, describe at least two moments of
happiness you had today.

1. _____

_____

_____

_____

_____

_____

_____

2. _____

_____

_____

_____

_____

_____

_____

Habit #3: **Happy people believe they are in control of their lives**

Assignment: How did I influence something I didn't think I had control over, or release something I couldn't control today?

_____

_____

_____

_____

_____

_____

_____

_____

When the morning's freshness has been replaced by the weariness of midday, when the muscles quiver under the strain, the climb seems endless, and, suddenly, nothing will go quite as you wish — it is then that you must not hesitate.
                                    – Dag Hammarskjold

3

Daily Moments of Happiness

Day _____   Date _____

In the space below, describe at least two moments of happiness you had today.

1. _____

   _____

   _____

   _____

   _____

   _____

2. _____

   _____

   _____

   _____

   _____

   _____

Habit #3: **Happy people believe they are in control of their lives**

Assignment: How did I influence something I didn't think I had control over, or release something I couldn't control today?

_____

_____

_____

_____

_____

_____

_____

_____

Looking honestly at the reality of the situation and seeing the positive in it enhances the quality of life. Self-motivated people look at each day as a new opportunity.

– Rick Pitino, *Success Is a Choice*

4

Happy People Are Outgoing

Then the day came when the risk
to remain tight in a bud was more
painful than the risk to blossom.

— Anais Nin

Whether people are outgoing because they are happy, or they are happy because they are outgoing, is not known for sure. But one thing *is* sure: When you take action, it affects you immediately, creating a change in attitude.

Say you get up in the morning, and the last thing you feel like doing is your morning exercise routine. You think, It's okay, I can take a day off, I deserve it. And you think about snuggling down into your nice warm, cozy bed. Instead of trying to change your thoughts, you get up, put your running shoes on, and get into action. Within seconds you will have an entirely different outlook on life. You will feel vibrant and alive.

You can take action today. In fact, if you want to make an important change, the way to do it is to get up and start acting outgoing today. It is the same thing with feeling happy and being outgoing. If we wait until the spirit moves us, it may not come until the 12th of never.

You don't have to wait until you feel outgoing, or be born an extrovert.

At first this may be uncomfortable. You might feel awkward, like you're being phony. It's like that when you learn any new skill. When you first learned to drive a car, did you hop behind the wheel and zoom off? No. Whoever was instructing you said, "Okay, now put the key in ignition." And you said, "What's the ignition?" But you kept at it and now you can drive a car while you also eat, talk on the phone, listen to music, and instruct other people how to drive through your hand signals.

If you hadn't kept in action, pushing through the discomfort, your mom would still be driving you on dates or taking you to work.

By acting as if you are outgoing today, you gain control of your emotional life. You are no longer a victim of outside events. Soon, what was once thought to be difficult or awkward becomes natural.

Assignment for This Week

At least one time each day write down an event when you consciously chose to extend yourself and be outgoing.

4

Daily Moments of Happiness

Day _____ Date _____

In the space below, describe at least two moments of happiness you had today.

1. _____

_____

_____

_____

_____

_____

_____

2. _____

_____

_____

_____

_____

_____

_____

Habit #4: **Happy people are outgoing**

Assignment: How was I outgoing today?

_____

_____

_____

_____

_____

_____

_____

_____

_____

_____

Cheerfulness, like spring, opens all the blossoms of the inward person.

– Jean Paul Richter

4

Daily Moments of Happiness

Day _____ Date _____

In the space below, describe at least two moments of happiness you had today.

1. _____

   _____

   _____

   _____

   _____

   _____

   _____

2. _____

   _____

   _____

   _____

   _____

   _____

   _____

Habit #4: **Happy people are outgoing**

Assignment: How was I outgoing today?

_____

_____

_____

_____

_____

_____

_____

_____

_____

_____

*Commitment is healthiest
not when it is without
doubt, but in spite of it.*

– Rollo May

4

Daily Moments of Happiness

Day _____ Date _____

In the space below, describe at least two moments of happiness you had today.

1. _____
_____
_____
_____
_____
_____
_____

2. _____
_____
_____
_____
_____
_____
_____

Habit #4: **Happy people are outgoing**

Assignment: How was I outgoing today?

_____

_____

_____

_____

_____

_____

_____

_____

_____

_____

_____

_____

Make happy those who are near,
and those who are far will come:

– Chinese proverb

4

Daily Moments of Happiness

Day _____   Date _____

In the space below, describe at least two moments of
happiness you had today.

1. _____

    _____

    _____

    _____

    _____

    _____

    _____

2. _____

    _____

    _____

    _____

    _____

    _____

    _____

Habit #4: **Happy people are outgoing**

Assignment: How was I outgoing today?

_____

_____

_____

_____

_____

_____

_____

_____

_____

_____

*The principal mark of genius
is not perfection but originality,
the opening of new frontiers.*

– Arthur Koestler

4

Daily Moments of Happiness

Day _____ Date _____

In the space below, describe at least two moments of happiness you had today.

1. _____

_____

_____

_____

_____

_____

2. _____

_____

_____

_____

_____

_____

_____

Habit #4: **Happy people are outgoing**

Assignment: How was I outgoing today?

_____

_____

_____

_____

_____

_____

_____

_____

_____

_____

_____

_____

Most people are about as happy
as they make up their mind to be.

– Abraham Lincoln

4

Daily Moments of Happiness

Day _____ Date _____

In the space below, describe at least two moments of happiness you had today.

1. _____

_____

_____

_____

_____

_____

2. _____

_____

_____

_____

_____

_____

Habit #4: **Happy people are outgoing**

Assignment: How was I outgoing today?

_____

_____

_____

_____

_____

_____

_____

_____

I believe the difference between great people and everyone else is that great people create their lives actively, while everyone else is created by their lives, passively waiting to see where life takes them next.

The difference between the two is the difference between living fully and just existing.

– Michael E. Gerber

4

Daily Moments of Happiness

Day _____ Date _____

In the space below, describe at least two moments of happiness you had today.

1. _____

   _____

   _____

   _____

   _____

   _____

2. _____

   _____

   _____

   _____

   _____

   _____

Habit #4: **Happy people are outgoing**

Assignment: How was I outgoing today?

_____

_____

_____

_____

_____

_____

_____

_____

_____

Security is mostly a superstition. It does not exist in nature, nor do the children of men as a whole experience it. Avoiding danger is no safer in the long run than outright exposure. The fearful are caught as often as the bold.

Life is either a daring adventure or nothing.

– Helen Keller

5

Happy People Know That the Best Things in Life Are Free

Each day is a gift to you. Make it blossom and grow into a thing of beauty.

— Heart Warmers

People spend thousands of dollars on vacations and leisure-time products and equipment. Yet, people say that their happiest times are when they are involved in activities that require little or no money. People feel good when they are talking with friends, or involved in hobbies. In fact, they tend to be less happy when they are involved with their expensive equipment.

One of the most enjoyable times of my life was when I had very little money. It was during that time that I realized how much I had counted on being able to buy things to make me happy. I could bring a smile to someone's face by bringing them a present. It made me feel in control when I could buy someone's lunch. It was scary when I had only myself to offer.

When you need money to gain approval, you never really feel accepted. You always wonder what people are really after.

Assignment for This Week

Each day write down a time when you enjoyed doing something that had nothing to do with money.

I think that what we're seeking is an experience of being alive, so that our life experiences on the purely physical plane will have resonance within our own innermost being and reality, so that we actually feel the rapture of being alive.

– Joseph Campbell

5
Daily Moments of Happiness

Day _____ Date _____

In the space below, describe at least two moments of happiness you had today.

1. _____

_____

_____

_____

_____

_____

2. _____

_____

_____

_____

_____

_____

Habit #5: **Happy people know that the best
things in life are free**

Assignment: What did I enjoy today that had nothing to
do with money?

_____

_____

_____

_____

_____

_____

_____

_____

_____

*It is easy to be independent when
you've got money. But to be
independent when you haven't
got a thing—that's the Lord's test.*

– Mahalia Jackson

5

Daily Moments of Happiness

Day _____ Date _____

In the space below, describe at least two moments of happiness you had today.

1. _____

_____

_____

_____

_____

_____

2. _____

_____

_____

_____

_____

_____

Habit #5:   **Happy people know that the best things in life are free**

Assignment: What did I enjoy today that had nothing to do with money?

_____

_____

_____

_____

_____

_____

_____

_____

_____

*Try not to become a
person of success —
rather, a person of value.*

– Albert Einstein

5

Daily Moments of Happiness

Day _____   Date _____

In the space below, describe at least two moments of happiness you had today.

1. _____

   _____

   _____

   _____

   _____

   _____

2. _____

   _____

   _____

   _____

   _____

   _____

Habit #5:   **Happy people know that the best
things in life are free**

Assignment: What did I enjoy today that had nothing to
do with money?

_____

_____

_____

_____

_____

_____

_____

_____

_____

*Life is better than death, I believe,
if only because it is less boring, and
because it has fresh peaches in it.*

– Alice Walker

5

Daily Moments of Happiness

Day _____   Date _____

In the space below, describe at least two moments of happiness you had today.

1. _____

_____

_____

_____

_____

_____

_____

2. _____

_____

_____

_____

_____

_____

_____

Habit #5: **Happy people know that the best things in life are free**

Assignment: What did I enjoy today that had nothing to do with money?

_____

_____

_____

_____

_____

_____

_____

_____

_____

_____

Joy is not in things;
it is in us.

– Wagner

5

Daily Moments of Happiness

Day _____ Date _____

In the space below, describe at least two moments of happiness you had today.

1. _____

_____

_____

_____

_____

_____

_____

2. _____

_____

_____

_____

_____

_____

_____

Habit #5:   **Happy people know that the best
things in life are free**

Assignment: What did I enjoy today that had nothing to
do with money?

_____

_____

_____

_____

_____

_____

_____

_____

*Be willing to learn . . . for the
rest of your life. It's essential.
Learning keeps you alert,
flexible, and growing.*

– Author unknown

121

5

Daily Moments of Happiness

Day _____   Date _____

In the space below, describe at least two moments of
happiness you had today.

1. _____

   _____

   _____

   _____

   _____

   _____

   _____

2. _____

   _____

   _____

   _____

   _____

   _____

   _____

Habit #5: **Happy people know that the best things in life are free**

Assignment: What did I enjoy today that had nothing to do with money?

_____

_____

_____

_____

_____

_____

_____

_____

_____

It's only possible to live happily ever after on a day-to-day basis.

– Margaret Bonnano

5

Daily Moments of Happiness

Day _____ Date _____

In the space below, describe at least two moments of happiness you had today.

1. _____

_____

_____

_____

_____

_____

2. _____

_____

_____

_____

_____

_____

Habit #5: **Happy people know that the best things in life are free**

Assignment: What did I enjoy today that had nothing to do with money?

_____

_____

_____

_____

_____

_____

_____

_____

_____

_____

_____

How simple it is to see that we can only be happy now, and there will never be a time when it is not now.

– Gerald Jampolsky

6

Happy People Are Friendly

*The most positive experiences people report
are usually with friends . . . People are usually
happier and more motivated when with friends,
regardless of what they are doing.*

– Mihaly Csikszentmihalyi

Happy people have friends in their life that they can
openly share themselves with. When you have people in
your life that you can relax with and just be okay the way
you are, you feel a sense of connectedness.

Close relationships also affect health. People who are
going through difficult times alone and don't talk about it
have more health problems than people who discuss their
difficulties.

Just as friendship reduces pain, it also increases happiness. When you have people who care about you, with
whom you can share not only your joys and sorrows but
all the events in your life, you feel a rightness with the
world. Surveys have determined that people are 60% more
likely to report that they are very happy when they have
five or more friends that they can discuss problems with.

Friendships are so important to the quality of life that they shouldn't be left to chance. The most rewarding friendships are those where you share goals and common interests, and find the time you spend together stimulating. Sometimes you meet someone you just "click" with, but you can't count on that. It usually takes extending yourself to increase friendships. One of the best ways of doing that is to be interested in other people and then sharing something of yourself. The more you do this the more chances you have to find the people that you do click with and enjoy spending time with.

Assignment for This Week

Each day write down one instance where you deepened your relationship with someone, by being interested in them or by sharing something of yourself.

6

Daily Moments of Happiness

Day _____ Date _____

In the space below, describe at least two moments of
happiness you had today.

1. _____

_____

_____

_____

_____

_____

2. _____

_____

_____

_____

_____

_____

Habit #6: **Happy people are friendly**

Assignment: Who did I deepen a relationship with, and how did I do it?

_____

_____

_____

_____

_____

_____

_____

_____

The more deeply you understand other people, the more you will appreciate them and the more reverent you will feel about them. To touch the soul of another human being is to walk on holy ground.

– Stephen Covey

6

Daily Moments of Happiness

Day _____   Date _____

In the space below, describe at least two moments of happiness you had today.

1. _____

_____

_____

_____

_____

_____

_____

2. _____

_____

_____

_____

_____

_____

_____

Habit #6: **Happy people are friendly**

Assignment: Who did I deepen a relationship with, and how did I do it?

_____

_____

_____

_____

_____

_____

_____

_____

Negativity is contagious, and you walk away feeling lousy after spending time in the company of a negative person. Positiveness is contagious as well, and spending time with a positive person makes you feel as though you can sprout wings and fly.
— Susan Jeffers, Ph.D.

6

Daily Moments of Happiness

Day _____ Date _____

In the space below, describe at least two moments of
happiness you had today.

1. _____

_____

_____

_____

_____

_____

2. _____

_____

_____

_____

_____

_____

Habit #6: **Happy people are friendly**

Assignment: Who did I deepen a relationship with, and how did I do it?

_____

_____

_____

_____

_____

_____

_____

_____

_____

A person is a person through another person's gift of happiness.

– Bantu proverb

6

Daily Moments of Happiness

Day _____ Date _____

In the space below, describe at least two moments of happiness you had today.

1. _____

_____

_____

_____

_____

_____

2. _____

_____

_____

_____

_____

_____

Habit #6: **Happy people are friendly**

Assignment: Who did I deepen a relationship with, and how did I do it?

_____

_____

_____

_____

_____

_____

_____

_____

_____

It is amazing how much happiness one smile can bring.

– Mother Teresa

6
Daily Moments of Happiness

Day _____ Date _____

In the space below, describe at least two moments of happiness you had today.

1. _____

_____

_____

_____

_____

_____

_____

2. _____

_____

_____

_____

_____

_____

_____

Habit #6: **Happy people are friendly**

Assignment: Who did I deepen a relationship with, and how did I do it?

_____

_____

_____

_____

_____

_____

_____

_____

Sometimes, with luck, we find the kind of true friend, male or female, that appears only two or three times in a lucky lifetime: one that will winter us and summer us, grieve, rejoice, and travel with us.

– Barbara Holland

137

6

Daily Moments of Happiness

Day _____ Date _____

In the space below, describe at least two moments of happiness you had today.

1. _____

_____

_____

_____

_____

_____

2. _____

_____

_____

_____

_____

_____

Habit #6: **Happy people are friendly**

Assignment: Who did I deepen a relationship with, and how did I do it?

_____

_____

_____

_____

_____

_____

_____

_____

_____

_____

Networking is an enrichment program, not an entitlement program.

– Susan RoAne

6

Daily Moments of Happiness

Day _____   Date _____

In the space below, describe at least two moments of happiness you had today.

1. _____

   _____

   _____

   _____

   _____

   _____

   _____

2. _____

   _____

   _____

   _____

   _____

   _____

   _____

Habit #6: **Happy people are friendly**

Assignment: Who did I deepen a relationship with, and how did I do it?

_____

_____

_____

_____

_____

_____

_____

_____

_____

_____

Let us always meet each other with a smile, for the smile is the beginning of love.
– Mother Teresa

7

Happy People Find a Reason to Laugh

A merry heart doeth good like medicine.

– William Shakespeare

In a hospital bed with an illness that one doctor had never seen anyone recover from, and another doctor had seen only one person in 500 recover from—and in such agony that he couldn't even move his thumbs without pain— Norman Cousins chose laughter as one of his primary courses of treatment.

Cousins knew that when people are depressed, they create a downward spiral that feeds on itself, increasing their depression and potential illness. He wondered if the opposite might also be true. When a person is happy does that feed on itself and create an upward spiral? In his inspiring book, *Anatomy of an Illness,* Cousins tells how watching Marx Brothers movies and other comedies for ten minutes provided him two hours of pain-free, medication-free, peaceful slumber.

Since that time, it has been proven that when people have a positive experience their immune systems carry the positive benefits for up to two days. A depressing experience lowers the immune system for more than a day.

Laughter also reduces the negative effect of stress, helps people deal with personal problems better, and increases creativity. In one study, a group was given a difficult problem to solve. Try as they would, they couldn't do it. After they were shown a short comedy film they found an innovative solution to the problem.

In addition, people retain 70% more information when it is presented with humor.

When we are able to laugh at ourselves, we feel better and more relaxed. When we laugh with friends, we feel an increased closeness. With all its benefits, laughter may not be a cure-all, but it sure makes us feel better about what ails us.

There are two basic types of humor. One type of humor diminishes people. It creates laughter at the expense of someone else or another group of people. Since a key part of the happiness habit is doing things that make a positive difference, this type of humor doesn't fit the bill.

The other type of humor reveals us to ourselves and makes us laugh at our faults. It allows us to accept ourselves and relate to other people. When you walk away from this kind of comedy show you feel better about yourself and the world.

Assignment for This Week

Each day write down a negative event that you consciously erased with laughter.

---●7●---

Daily Moments of Happiness

Day _____ Date _____

In the space below, describe at least two moments of happiness you had today.

1. _____

_____

_____

_____

_____

_____

2. _____

_____

_____

_____

_____

_____

144

Habit #7: **Happy people find a reason to laugh**

Assignment: How did I consciously erase a negative event with laughter today?

_____

_____

_____

_____

_____

_____

_____

_____

_____

_____

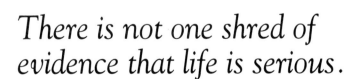

There is not one shred of evidence that life is serious.

– Brendan Gill

7

Daily Moments of Happiness

Day _____ Date _____

In the space below, describe at least two moments of
happiness you had today.

1. _____

_____

_____

_____

_____

_____

_____

2. _____

_____

_____

_____

_____

_____

_____

Habit #7: **Happy people find a reason to laugh**

Assignment: How did I consciously erase a negative event with laughter today?

_____

_____

_____

_____

_____

_____

_____

_____

A few minutes of laughing lowers stress hormones and raises the number of circulating antibodies that fight off disease . . . Simple enjoyable activities, such as having a few friends over for dinner or sharing a sunset with a loved one, can have immediate results such as strengthening the immune system and temporarily reducing blood pressure.

– Paul Pearsall, Ph.D., *The Pleasure Prescription*

7

Daily Moments of Happiness

Day _____   Date _____

In the space below, describe at least two moments of
happiness you had today.

1. _____

_____

_____

_____

_____

_____

2. _____

_____

_____

_____

_____

_____

Habit #7: **Happy people find a reason to laugh**

Assignment: How did I consciously erase a negative event with laughter today?

_____

_____

_____

_____

_____

_____

_____

_____

_____

_____

Against the assault of laughter nothing can stand.

– Mark Twain

7

Daily Moments of Happiness

Day _____ Date _____

In the space below, describe at least two moments of happiness you had today.

1. _____

_____

_____

_____

_____

_____

_____

2. _____

_____

_____

_____

_____

_____

_____

Habit #7: **Happy people find a reason to laugh**

Assignment: How did I consciously erase a negative event with laughter today?

_____

_____

_____

_____

_____

_____

_____

_____

_____

_____

One loses many laughs
by not laughing at oneself.

– Sara Jeannette Duncan

7

Daily Moments of Happiness

Day _____ Date _____

In the space below, describe at least two moments of happiness you had today.

1. _____

_____

_____

_____

_____

_____

2. _____

_____

_____

_____

_____

_____

Habit #7: **Happy people find a reason to laugh**

Assignment: How did I consciously erase a negative event with laughter today?

_____

_____

_____

_____

_____

_____

_____

_____

_____

_____

Laughter can be more satisfying than honor, more precious than money, more heart-cleansing than prayer.

– Harriet Rochlin

7

Daily Moments of Happiness

Day _____ Date _____

In the space below, describe at least two moments of
happiness you had today.

1. _____

_____

_____

_____

_____

_____

_____

2. _____

_____

_____

_____

_____

_____

_____

Habit #7: **Happy people find a reason to laugh**

Assignment: How did I consciously erase a negative
event with laughter today?

_____

_____

_____

_____

_____

_____

_____

_____

_____

_____

_____

*There is no cure for birth and
death save to enjoy the interval.*

– George Santayana

155

7

Daily Moments of Happiness

Day _____ Date _____

In the space below, describe at least two moments of happiness you had today.

1. _____

_____

_____

_____

_____

_____

_____

2. _____

_____

_____

_____

_____

_____

_____

Habit #7: **Happy people find a reason to laugh**

Assignment: How did I consciously erase a negative
event with laughter today?

_____

_____

_____

_____

_____

_____

_____

_____

_____

*Life is not THAT serious.
Let's take our humor more
seriously.*

– Andrew Mathews,
Being Happy

Happy People Experience "The Flow" in Their Work

It is not enough to be happy to have an excellent life. The point is to be happy while doing things that stretch our skills, that help us grow and fulfill our potential.

— Mihaly Csikszentmihalyi

What is more exhilarating than being totally absorbed in an important and challenging project that uses skills you are good at? Those are parts of the conditions of "flow," an experience happiness expert Mihaly Csikszentmihalyi has been studying for over two decades.

However, don't count on always feeling happy during the course of a challenge. As one football coach said, "I never saw a man make a tackle with a smile on his face." It's the completion of a difficult and meaningful project that is one of life's great pleasures.

The problem is that much of our life is filled up with doing trivial, routine, unimportant, and frequently boring work. Bringing the flow experience to whatever projects you are working on can be difficult and take discipline, but developing the habit can give you such a rich, rewarding, and joyous experience in life that it is well worth the effort. By combining the elements of flow in your job, you can turn a dull task into an enjoyable project that you look forward to.

Flow happens when you have a clear goal and rules for action. You also have immediate feedback on how you're doing, are using skills that you are good at, and are facing a challenge. These magical moments occur when you get so involved that you lose track of time.

If your work situation is not to your liking there two possibilities: one is to change your job, the other is to change your attitude. Many times it's not the job, it's our attitude toward it that makes the difference. Even the most exciting job becomes boring after a while.

The simplest way to bring enjoyment to any job is to create challenges or games out of whatever project or task you are working on. This can be as simple as setting a time goal—for anything from how long it takes you to peel carrots to how long it takes you to put a delightful meal together for your family. If you're a waiter, a challenge could be how many expressions of appreciation you can generate from customers per night through your fabulous service. If you're a manager you could challenge yourself to find ways to increase productivity while increasing employee satisfaction at the same time.

Assignment for This Week

Each day write down one challenge or game you set for yourself and what difference it made to create a challenge.

8

Daily Moments of Happiness

Day _____ Date _____

In the space below, describe at least two moments of happiness you had today.

1. _____

_____

_____

_____

_____

_____

2. _____

_____

_____

_____

_____

_____

_____

Habit #8: **Happy people experience "the flow" in their lives**

Assignment: What challenge did I set for myself today? What difference did it make?

_____

_____

_____

_____

_____

_____

_____

_____

_____

Imagination is more important than knowledge.

– Einstein

Imagination rules the world.

– Disraeli

8

Daily Moments of Happiness

Day _____ Date _____

In the space below, describe at least two moments of happiness you had today.

1. _____

_____

_____

_____

_____

_____

_____

2. _____

_____

_____

_____

_____

_____

_____

Habit #8: **Happy people experience "the flow" in their lives**

Assignment: What challenge did I set for myself today? What difference did it make?

_____

_____

_____

_____

_____

_____

_____

Challenge connotes a very special kind of engagement of our spirit. It includes a willingness and an eagerness to do battle—but in a positive, non-distressful way.

The response is a willingness to put oneself on the line without fear. The emotional feelings are not toxic, unpleasant, or distasteful. To the contrary, feelings of challenge, fun, enjoyment, and risk become intimately bound together.

— James E. Loehr, *Stress for Success*

8

Daily Moments of Happiness

Day _____ Date _____

In the space below, describe at least two moments of happiness you had today.

1. _____

_____

_____

_____

_____

_____

_____

2. _____

_____

_____

_____

_____

_____

_____

Habit #8: **Happy people experience "the flow" in their lives**

Assignment: What challenge did I set for myself today? What difference did it make?

———————————————————————

———————————————————————

———————————————————————

———————————————————————

———————————————————————

———————————————————————

———————————————————————

———————————————————————

———————————————————————

———————————————————————

All you have to do to change your world is to change the way you think about it.

– Susan Jeffers, Ph.D.

8

Daily Moments of Happiness

Day _____ Date _____

In the space below, describe at least two moments of happiness you had today.

1. _____

_____

_____

_____

_____

_____

_____

2. _____

_____

_____

_____

_____

_____

_____

Habit #8:   **Happy people experience "the flow" in their lives**

Assignment: What challenge did I set for myself today? What difference did it make?

_____

_____

_____

_____

_____

_____

_____

_____

_____

_____

Challenges make you discover things about yourself that you never really knew.
                                    – Cicely Tyson

8

Daily Moments of Happiness

Day _____   Date _____

In the space below, describe at least two moments of
happiness you had today.

1. _____

_____

_____

_____

_____

_____

2. _____

_____

_____

_____

_____

_____

Habit #8: **Happy people experience "the flow" in their lives**

Assignment: What challenge did I set for myself today? What difference did it make?

_____

_____

_____

_____

_____

_____

_____

_____

It's not how you feel, but what you do that counts. Because when you do the right things, feelings tend to improve as a matter of course. But spend too much time being overly concerned about uncomfortable feelings, and you may never get around to doing what it takes to actually improve. Focus your attention on the mental and physical actions that will improve your life.

– Jeffrey M. Schwartz, _Brain Lock_

8

Daily Moments of Happiness

Day _____ Date _____

In the space below, describe at least two moments of happiness you had today.

1. _____

_____

_____

_____

_____

_____

2. _____

_____

_____

_____

_____

_____

Habit #8: **Happy people experience "the flow"
in their lives**

Assignment: What challenge did I set for myself today?
What difference did it make?

_____

_____

_____

_____

_____

_____

_____

*It is a mistake to look too
far ahead. Only one link
in the chain of destiny can
be handled at a time.*

– Winston Churchill

8
Daily Moments of Happiness

Day _____ Date _____

In the space below, describe at least two moments of
happiness you had today.

1. _____

_____

_____

_____

_____

_____

2. _____

_____

_____

_____

_____

_____

Habit #8: **Happy people experience "the flow" in their lives**

Assignment: What challenge did I set for myself today? What difference did it make?

_____

_____

_____

_____

_____

_____

_____

_____

_____

_____

Death is not the greatest loss in life. The greatest loss is what dies inside us while we live.

– Norman Cousins

9

Happy People Spread Their Joy

Appreciation, applause, approval, respect — we all love it!

– Tom Peters

"The deepest craving of human beings is the desire to be appreciated." That's perhaps the most important thing William James, the father of modern-day psychology, had to say at the end of his remarkable career. This means day in and day out you can meet people's deepest desires by simply telling them what you appreciate about them.

Yet, if you ask husbands, wives, children, mothers, fathers, employees, and bosses how often they receive compliments, they'll tell you, "Hardly ever. People always tell me what's wrong, but they never tell me when I do anything right." When researchers have taken the time to observe what people really do, they discovered that people usually give four negative comments for every positive one! So what people have been saying all along, "They only tell me when I do it wrong!" is really true.

If you are the bearer of negative comments, you most likely won't be creating a happy environment. It will negatively affect you as well as the people around you. If you take the time to let people know what you do appreciate, they will be more open to suggestions for improvement.

When you appreciate others, it doesn't just affect them —it affects you too. One time I was having an argument with my husband. I was furious with him. I walked into my office and closed the door to be alone and mull over his bad points. As I sat down I saw my happiness habit book. For some reason I picked it up and started to write down some of what I loved about my husband. To my surprise I started feeling warm and loving feelings toward him. I felt so good about him that I went in and told him I loved him. That was the end of an argument that otherwise would have gone on much longer.

When you thank people and let them know how much you appreciate them, you brighten their world. It's important to be specific. When you just give general praise— such as "you're terrific" or "that's wonderful"—it can make people anxious because they're not sure what you're talking about, and it can be manipulative.

However, when you let people know specifically what they did and why you appreciate it, they blossom like beautiful flowers.

Assignment for This Week

Each day this week write down at least one time that you complimented someone and how it felt.

9

Daily Moments of Happiness

Day _____   Date _____

In the space below, describe at least two moments of happiness you had today.

1. _____

    _____

    _____

    _____

    _____

    _____

2. _____

    _____

    _____

    _____

    _____

    _____

Habit #9: **Happy people spread their joy**

Assignment: Who did I compliment today? What did I say or do, and how did it feel to show my appreciation?

_____

_____

_____

_____

_____

_____

_____

_____

_____

_____

When we encourage celebration of simple joys and recognition of small wins, we help create an atmosphere where initiative is alive and vibrant.

– Brian D. Biro

9

Daily Moments of Happiness

Day _____ Date _____

In the space below, describe at least two moments of happiness you had today.

1. _____

_____

_____

_____

_____

_____

2. _____

_____

_____

_____

_____

_____

Habit #9: **Happy people spread their joy**

Assignment: Who did I compliment today? What did I say or do, and how did it feel to show my appreciation?

_____

_____

_____

_____

_____

_____

_____

_____

_____

You give but little when you give of your possessions. It is when you give of yourself that you truly give.

– Kahlil Gibran

9

Daily Moments of Happiness

Day _____ Date _____

In the space below, describe at least two moments of happiness you had today.

1. _____

_____

_____

_____

_____

_____

_____

2. _____

_____

_____

_____

_____

_____

_____

Habit #9: **Happy people spread their joy**

Assignment: Who did I compliment today? What did I say or do, and how did it feel to show my appreciation?

_____

_____

_____

_____

_____

_____

_____

_____

_____

_____

Give unconditionally whatever a person needs in the moment. The point is to do something, however small, and show you care through your actions by giving your time.

– Mother Teresa

9

Daily Moments of Happiness

Day _____ Date _____

In the space below, describe at least two moments of happiness you had today.

1. _____

   _____

   _____

   _____

   _____

   _____

   _____

2. _____

   _____

   _____

   _____

   _____

   _____

Habit #9: **Happy people spread their joy**

Assignment: Who did I compliment today? What did I say or do, and how did it feel to show my appreciation?

_____

_____

_____

_____

_____

_____

_____

_____

_____

_____

Positive people can take on the world.

– Rick Pitino,
Success Is a Choice

9

Daily Moments of Happiness

Day _____   Date _____

In the space below, describe at least two moments of happiness you had today.

1. _____

_____

_____

_____

_____

_____

2. _____

_____

_____

_____

_____

_____

Habit #9: **Happy people spread their joy**

Assignment: Who did I compliment today? What did I say or do, and how did it feel to show my appreciation?

_____

_____

_____

_____

_____

_____

_____

_____

_____

My paramount object was to make people happy. To see someone smile, to feel that another man's heartbeat was for me, was to me a source of immeasurable happiness.

– Anwar Sadat

9

Daily Moments of Happiness

Day _____ Date _____

In the space below, describe at least two moments of happiness you had today.

1. _____
   _____
   _____
   _____
   _____
   _____
   _____

2. _____
   _____
   _____
   _____
   _____
   _____
   _____

Habit #9: **Happy people spread their joy**

Assignment: Who did I compliment today? What did I say or do, and how did it feel to show my appreciation?

_____

_____

_____

_____

_____

_____

_____

_____

When you exercise your initiative, it is incredibly empowering for you and those you touch. One of the most valuable ways to exercise your initiative is to acknowledge and recognize initiative in others.

– Brian D. Biro

9

Daily Moments of Happiness

Day _____ Date _____

In the space below, describe at least two moments of
happiness you had today.

1. _____

   _____

   _____

   _____

   _____

   _____

2. _____

   _____

   _____

   _____

   _____

   _____

Habit #9: **Happy people spread their joy**

Assignment: Who did I compliment today? What did I say or do, and how did it feel to show my appreciation?

_____

_____

_____

_____

_____

_____

_____

_____

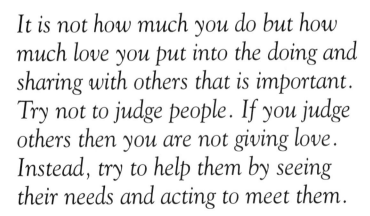

It is not how much you do but how much love you put into the doing and sharing with others that is important. Try not to judge people. If you judge others then you are not giving love. Instead, try to help them by seeing their needs and acting to meet them.

– Mother Teresa

189

10

Happy People Control Their Impulses

*Old urges will continue to arise,
perhaps for years. Urges do not
matter, actions do.*

— Dan Millman

How do you feel when you have eaten that extra piece of cake, reacted in anger too quickly, or procrastinated on an important project that's already overdue? Anxious? Guilty? Worried? The ability to control your impulses or delay gratification in pursuit of a goal will not only bring you happiness and self-trust, it is a critical skill for success.

We live in a culture that feels entitled to have our wants and needs met instantly, and has little patience for the kind of time, energy, and attention it takes to produce a job well done. When it gets uncomfortable or frustrating we think something is wrong—that it shouldn't be this way—and give up. Our desire for instant gratification and our unwillingness to tolerate discomfort undermines self-confidence, success, and happiness.

By learning to control your impulses you have power over yourself. A key element in controlling impulses is to be able to distinguish between feelings and action. They often come so closely together that it's hard to separate them. For example, you feel like having that extra piece of chocolate and, before you know it, your mouth is full. You're facing an annoying and difficult problem, and all of the sudden you find yourself needing to sharpen all your pencils perfectly.

You have chosen to take refuge in doing what's comfortable and avoiding the frustrating feelings that go along with challenging situations. You have also chosen the negative consequences that go with giving up on a goal: not only losing out on the rewards of attaining your goal, but diminishing your self-confidence as well. And, because behaving in that way increases the likelihood that you will do it again, you have also strengthened your avoidance muscle.

By learning to delay gratification and completing desired actions and projects, no matter how small or large, you increase your power to create your destiny.

Assignment for This Week

Each day this week write down at least one time when you recognized a non-productive impulse and chose the action that was in your best interest rather than following a self-defeating impulse.

10

Daily Moments of Happiness

Day _____ Date _____

In the space below, describe at least two moments of happiness you had today.

1. _____

_____

_____

_____

_____

_____

_____

2. _____

_____

_____

_____

_____

_____

_____

Habit #10: **Happy people control their impulses**

Assignment: What non-productive impulse did I
recognize? How did I handle it?

_____

_____

_____

_____

_____

_____

_____

_____

*There is perhaps no psychological skill more funda-
mental than resisting impulse. It is the root of all
emotional self-control, since all emotions, by their
very nature, lead to one or another impulse to act . . .
Goal-directed, self-imposed delay of gratification
is perhaps the essence of emotional self-regulation:
the ability to deny impulse in the service of a goal,
whether it be building a business, solving an algebraic
equation, or pursuing the Stanley Cup.*

– Martin E.P. Seligman

10

Daily Moments of Happiness

Day _____ Date _____

In the space below, describe at least two moments of happiness you had today.

1. _____

_____

_____

_____

_____

_____

_____

2. _____

_____

_____

_____

_____

_____

_____

Habit #10: **Happy people control their impulses**

Assignment: What non-productive impulse did I recognize? How did I handle it?

_____

_____

_____

_____

_____

_____

_____

_____

_____

You never conquer the mountain.
You only conquer yourself.

– Jim Whittaker, first American
to climb Mount Everest

10

Daily Moments of Happiness

Day _____ Date _____

In the space below, describe at least two moments of happiness you had today.

1. _____

_____

_____

_____

_____

_____

_____

2. _____

_____

_____

_____

_____

_____

_____

Habit #10: **Happy people control their impulses**

Assignment: What non-productive impulse did I recognize? How did I handle it?

_____

_____

_____

_____

_____

_____

_____

_____

_____

Joy is what happens to us when we allow ourselves to recognize how good things really are.
– Marianne Williamson

10

Daily Moments of Happiness

Day _____ Date _____

In the space below, describe at least two moments of happiness you had today.

1. _____

_____

_____

_____

_____

_____

_____

2. _____

_____

_____

_____

_____

_____

_____

Habit #10: **Happy people control their impulses**

Assignment: What non-productive impulse did I recognize? How did I handle it?

_____

_____

_____

_____

_____

_____

_____

_____

_____

_____

Growth itself contains the germ of happiness.

– Pearl S. Buck

10

Daily Moments of Happiness

Day _____ Date _____

In the space below, describe at least two moments of happiness you had today.

1. _____

_____

_____

_____

_____

_____

2. _____

_____

_____

_____

_____

_____

Habit #10: **Happy people control their impulses**

Assignment: What non-productive impulse did I
recognize? How did I handle it?

_____

_____

_____

_____

_____

_____

_____

_____

_____

*Self-respect is the fruit of
discipline; the sense of
dignity grows with the
ability to say no to oneself.*

– Author unknown

10

Daily Moments of Happiness

Day _____ Date _____

In the space below, describe at least two moments of happiness you had today.

1. _____

_____

_____

_____

_____

_____

_____

2. _____

_____

_____

_____

_____

_____

_____

Habit #10: **Happy people control their impulses**

Assignment: What non-productive impulse did I recognize? How did I handle it?

Make each day your masterpiece.

– John Wooden

10

Daily Moments of Happiness

Day _____ Date _____

In the space below, describe at least two moments of happiness you had today.

1. _____

_____

_____

_____

_____

_____

2. _____

_____

_____

_____

_____

_____

Habit #10: **Happy people control their impulses**

Assignment: What non-productive impulse did I
recognize? How did I handle it?

_____

_____

_____

_____

_____

_____

_____

_____

_____

*Parents can only give good advice
or put their children on the right
paths, but the final forming of a
person's character lies in their
own hands.* — Anne Frank

11

Happy People Know That Love Makes the World Go Round

Love does not die easily. It is a living thing. It thrives in the face of all life's hazards, save one—neglect.

– James Bryden

There is probably no greater source of well-being or cause of misery than close, intimate, loving relationships. When things are working well, life is wonderful. When you are in conflict, it drains your energy and casts a cloud over life.

Study after study has consistently shown that people in stable, loving relationships are happier and more satisfied with their lives.[5] Committed relationships provide support, companionship, and intimacy.

A close, loving relationship has such a big impact on the overall quality of your life, it is critical to take the time and energy required to make it work. With divorce

---

[5] Myers, David G. *The Pursuit of Happiness*. New York: Avon Books, 1992, page 156.

statistics running about 50% for first marriages and 60% for second marriages, people seem to be willing to throw in the towel pretty easily. Sometimes that's the right thing to do. But most of the time you find the same or even worse problems in a new relationship because the issue is not the person, it's how you relate to problems. It is amazing what can happen when you work on the right areas.

A friend of mine was at the end of her rope, and in divorce court a year ago, when she and her husband decided to give it one last try. They are back together and with a deeper and more profound love than they ever had before. The power and reward of a good relationship is the ability to work through problems together and being committed to each other's happiness.

Two things that make a difference are:

1. *Your own happiness:* When you are feeling good about yourself, you are more likely to feel good about your relationship and less likely to invite conflict.

2. *Appreciation:* Focusing on what you like and love about your loved one will make that more present in your relationship.

Assignment for This Week

Each day write down something positive you did to increase a loved one's happiness, or to increase your happiness with them.

11

Daily Moments of Happiness

Day _____ Date _____

In the space below, describe at least two moments of
happiness you had today.

1. _____

_____

_____

_____

_____

_____

_____

2. _____

_____

_____

_____

_____

_____

_____

Habit #11: **Happy people know that love makes the world go round**

Assignment: What did I do to increase happiness with a loved one today?

_____

_____

_____

_____

_____

_____

_____

If you can't solve your problems, you will become discouraged; and you will believe that, since you can't solve your problems, you can't be happy. A better plan is to focus on what you want from your relationship, paying most attention to the strong parts of it, putting your efforts into creating happiness rather than diminishing unhappiness.

– Susan Page, *How One of You Can Bring the Two of You Together*

11

Daily Moments of Happiness

Day _____ Date _____

In the space below, describe at least two moments of happiness you had today.

1. _____

_____

_____

_____

_____

_____

_____

2. _____

_____

_____

_____

_____

_____

_____

Habit #11: **Happy people know that love makes the world go round**

Assignment: What did I do to increase happiness with a loved one today?

_____

_____

_____

_____

_____

_____

_____

_____

_____

*Love is the human safeguard
against all social pitfalls . . .
To love means to give, and
to give means to build, while
to hate is to destroy.*

– Anwar Sadat

11
Daily Moments of Happiness

Day _____ Date _____

In the space below, describe at least two moments of happiness you had today.

1. _____

_____

_____

_____

_____

_____

2. _____

_____

_____

_____

_____

_____

Habit #11: **Happy people know that love makes the world go round**

Assignment: What did I do to increase happiness with a loved one today?

_____

_____

_____

_____

_____

_____

_____

_____

_____

*The supreme happiness
of life is the conviction
that we are loved.*

– Victor Hugo

213

11

Daily Moments of Happiness

Day _____   Date _____

In the space below, describe at least two moments of
happiness you had today.

1. _____

   _____

   _____

   _____

   _____

   _____

   _____

2. _____

   _____

   _____

   _____

   _____

   _____

   _____

Habit #11: **Happy people know that love makes the world go round**

Assignment: What did I do to increase happiness with a loved one today?

_____

_____

_____

_____

_____

_____

_____

_____

_____

_____

Love doesn't make the world go round. Love is what makes the ride worthwhile.

– Franklin P. Jones

11

Daily Moments of Happiness

Day _____   Date _____

In the space below, describe at least two moments of happiness you had today.

1. _____

_____

_____

_____

_____

_____

_____

2. _____

_____

_____

_____

_____

_____

_____

Habit #11: **Happy people know that love makes
the world go round**

Assignment: What did I do to increase happiness with a
loved one today?

_____

_____

_____

_____

_____

_____

_____

_____

_____

_____

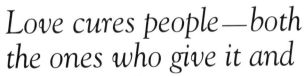

_Love cures people—both
the ones who give it and
the ones who receive it._

– Karl Menninger

11

Daily Moments of Happiness

Day _____   Date _____

In the space below, describe at least two moments of happiness you had today.

1. _____

_____

_____

_____

_____

_____

2. _____

_____

_____

_____

_____

_____

Habit #11: **Happy people know that love makes the world go round**

Assignment: What did I do to increase happiness with a loved one today?

_____

_____

_____

_____

_____

_____

_____

_____

_____

The heart that loves is always young.

– Author unknown

11

Daily Moments of Happiness

Day _____ Date _____

In the space below, describe at least two moments of happiness you had today.

1. _____

_____

_____

_____

_____

_____

2. _____

_____

_____

_____

_____

_____

_____

Habit #11: **Happy people know that love makes the world go round**

Assignment: What did I do to increase happiness with a loved one today?

_____

_____

_____

_____

_____

_____

_____

_____

_____

_____

We can only learn to love by loving.

– Iris Murdoch

12

Happy People
Are Enthusiastic

*Every success I have ever had
is because I begin each new day
and each new challenge with
childlike enthusiasm.*

– Terry Bradshaw

Every year over one billion people watch the Super Bowl. It is the highest-paid television commercial airtime of the year. It's talked about for weeks and months. People eagerly watch the playoffs to see who will go to the Super Bowl, and they pay outrageous sums of money to attend the game.

When you really examine it, there is no inherent reason why the Super Bowl is so exciting. But it is something to rally around and get excited about because it is fun to get excited and be involved.

We usually associate excitement with an outside event that happens. This week the purpose is to develop your own enthusiasm instead of waiting for something outside of you to make it happen.

222

Assignment for This Week

Each day this week write down one time when you got enthusiastic about something.

We act as though comfort and luxury were the chief require-ments of life, when all that we need to make us really happy is something to be enthusiastic about.

— Charles Kingsley

12

Daily Moments of Happiness

Day _____   Date _____

In the space below, describe at least two moments of happiness you had today.

1. _____

   _____

   _____

   _____

   _____

   _____

   _____

2. _____

   _____

   _____

   _____

   _____

   _____

   _____

Habit #12: **Happy people are enthusiastic**

Assignment: What did I get enthusiastic about today?

_____

_____

_____

_____

_____

_____

_____

_____

_____

_____

_____

_____

*Nothing great was
ever achieved without
enthusiasm.*

– Ralph Waldo Emerson

225

12

Daily Moments of Happiness

Day _____   Date _____

In the space below, describe at least two moments of
happiness you had today.

1. _____

   _____

   _____

   _____

   _____

   _____

   _____

2. _____

   _____

   _____

   _____

   _____

   _____

   _____

Habit #12: **Happy people are enthusiastic**

Assignment: What did I get enthusiastic about today?

_____

_____

_____

_____

_____

_____

_____

_____

_____

_____

Years wrinkle the skin,
but lack of enthusiasm
wrinkles the soul.

– Norman Vincent Peale

227

12

Daily Moments of Happiness

Day _____   Date _____

In the space below, describe at least two moments of happiness you had today.

1. _____

_____

_____

_____

_____

_____

_____

2. _____

_____

_____

_____

_____

_____

_____

Habit #12: **Happy people are enthusiastic**

Assignment: What did I get enthusiastic about today?

_____

_____

_____

_____

_____

_____

_____

_____

_____

_____

_____

*Flaming enthusiasm, backed up
by horse sense and persistence,
is the quality that most frequently
makes for success.*
— Dale Carnegie

12

Daily Moments of Happiness

Day _____   Date _____

In the space below, describe at least two moments of happiness you had today.

1. _____

   _____

   _____

   _____

   _____

   _____

2. _____

   _____

   _____

   _____

   _____

   _____

Habit #12: **Happy people are enthusiastic**

Assignment: What did I get enthusiastic about today?

_____

_____

_____

_____

_____

_____

_____

_____

_____

_____

_____

You will do foolish things, but do them with enthusiasm.

– Colette

12

Daily Moments of Happiness

Day _____   Date _____

In the space below, describe at least two moments of happiness you had today.

1. _____

_____

_____

_____

_____

_____

_____

2. _____

_____

_____

_____

_____

_____

_____

Habit #12: **Happy people are enthusiastic**

Assignment: What did I get enthusiastic about today?

_____

_____

_____

_____

_____

_____

_____

_____

_____

_____

*You communicate your
enthusiasm through your
words, voice quality, and
body language.*
— Brian D. Biro

12

Daily Moments of Happiness

Day _____ Date _____

In the space below, describe at least two moments of happiness you had today.

1. _____

_____

_____

_____

_____

_____

_____

2. _____

_____

_____

_____

_____

_____

_____

Habit #12: **Happy people are enthusiastic**

Assignment: What did I get enthusiastic about today?

_____

_____

_____

_____

_____

_____

_____

_____

_____

_____

_____

*Never underestimate
the power of passion.*

– Eve Sawyer

12

Daily Moments of Happiness

Day _____   Date _____

In the space below, describe at least two moments of
happiness you had today.

1. _____

   _____

   _____

   _____

   _____

   _____

   _____

2. _____

   _____

   _____

   _____

   _____

   _____

   _____

Habit #12: **Happy people are enthusiastic**

Assignment: What did I get enthusiastic about today?

_____

_____

_____

_____

_____

_____

_____

_____

_____

_____

_____

*Just think how happy you would be
if you lost everything and everyone
you have right now — and then
somehow got it back again.*

– Kobi Yamada

13

Happy People Know
What Their Life is All About

*How wonderful it is that nobody
need wait a single moment before
starting to improve the world.*

– Anne Frank

Is it enough to devote your life to making yourself happy? Whether it is enough or not is irrelevant. What's important is that it will not make you happy. Spending your life in pursuit of mindless pleasure will leave you feeling empty, lonely, and asking, "Is that all there is?" What adds vibrancy and meaning to life is to have a purpose greater than yourself that directs your life and your actions.

In *First Things First,* Stephen Covey talks about how he considers a personal mission statement essential to a well-lived life. A mission is like a guiding star. It gives you guidelines for how to operate in the world. Oprah Winfrey has many wonderful qualities, but I believe what gives her the greatest power is her relentless, unwavering mission to do what she can to improve the quality of life for people.

When you have a goal or a challenge that is big enough to include everything you do, it adds meaning and significance to your life. When you know that what you do matters, it is easier and more enjoyable to get into action.

The only person who can decide what your life is about is you. You make an impact on everyone you come in contact with. The choice you have is whether you will contribute to improving the quality of life or diminish it. It can be as simple as doing an excellent job raising your children or making sure you do a good job at whatever you are doing. There are thousands of ways to make a positive difference in the world: big ones and small ones.

Assignment for This Week

Each day write down a time when you have actively chosen to do something to make a positive difference in your world.

13

Daily Moments of Happiness

Day _____ Date _____

In the space below, describe at least two moments of happiness you had today.

1. _____

   _____

   _____

   _____

   _____

   _____

   _____

2. _____

   _____

   _____

   _____

   _____

   _____

   _____

Habit #13: **Happy people know what their life is all about**

Assignment: What did I do to make a positive difference in the world around me today?

_____

_____

_____

_____

_____

_____

_____

_____

_____

There is not a person alive who is not capable of greatly contributing to the well-being of this planet. Just changing your attitude can affect the world around you.

– Susan Jeffers, Ph.D.

13

Daily Moments of Happiness

Day _____   Date _____

In the space below, describe at least two moments of happiness you had today.

1. _____

_____

_____

_____

_____

_____

_____

2. _____

_____

_____

_____

_____

_____

_____

Habit #13: **Happy people know what their life is all about**

Assignment: What did I do to make a positive difference in the world around me today?

_____

_____

_____

_____

_____

_____

_____

_____

_____

_____

The courageous person acts for the sake of that which is noble.

– Paul Tillich, *The Courage to Be*

13

Daily Moments of Happiness

Day _____ Date _____

In the space below, describe at least two moments of
happiness you had today.

1. _____

_____

_____

_____

_____

_____

2. _____

_____

_____

_____

_____

_____

Habit #13: **Happy people know what their life
is all about**

Assignment: What did I do to make a positive difference
in the world around me today?

_____

_____

_____

_____

_____

_____

_____

_____

_____

_____

*The creation of a thousand
forests is in one acorn.*

– Ralph Waldo Emerson

13

Daily Moments of Happiness

Day _____ Date _____

In the space below, describe at least two moments of happiness you had today.

1. _____

_____

_____

_____

_____

_____

2. _____

_____

_____

_____

_____

_____

Habit #13: **Happy people know what their life is all about**

Assignment: What did I do to make a positive difference in the world around me today?

_____

_____

_____

_____

_____

_____

_____

_____

_____

_____

Life is a petty thing unless it is moved by the indomitable urge to extend its boundaries.

– Ortega y Gasset

13

Daily Moments of Happiness

Day _____   Date _____

In the space below, describe at least two moments of
happiness you had today.

1. _____

   _____

   _____

   _____

   _____

   _____

2. _____

   _____

   _____

   _____

   _____

   _____

   _____

Habit #13: **Happy people know what their life is all about**

Assignment: What did I do to make a positive difference in the world around me today?

_____

_____

_____

_____

_____

_____

_____

_____

_____

If we want progress, then we must provide the energy, the momentum, to reverse decay. By sheer force of will, because we are the planet's consciousness, we will make the world hang together.

– Margaret Wheatley

13

Daily Moments of Happiness

Day _____ Date _____

In the space below, describe at least two moments of happiness you had today.

1. _____

_____

_____

_____

_____

_____

2. _____

_____

_____

_____

_____

_____

Habit #13: **Happy people know what their life is all about**

Assignment: What did I do to make a positive difference in the world around me today?

_____

_____

_____

_____

_____

_____

_____

_____

_____

_____

There is no duty we so much under-rate as the duty of being happy. By being happy we sow anonymous benefits upon the world.

– Robert Louis Stevenson

13

Daily Moments of Happiness

Day _____ Date _____

In the space below, describe at least two moments of happiness you had today.

1. _____

_____

_____

_____

_____

_____

_____

2. _____

_____

_____

_____

_____

_____

_____

Habit #13: **Happy people know what their life is all about**

Assignment: What did I do to make a positive difference in the world around me today?

_____

_____

_____

_____

_____

_____

_____

_____

_____

_____

We become happier, much happier, when we realize that life is an opportunity rather than an obligation.

– Mary Augustine

SECTION 2
The HabitBuilder
Tool Chest

*Of all virtues we can learn, no trait is
more useful, more essential to survival,
and more likely to improve the quality
of life than the ability to transform
adversity into an enjoyable challenge.*

— Mihaly Csikszentmihalyi

I got some bad news this morning and I felt down and
unhappy. Then I was unhappy that I felt unhappy. I
thought, Oh no, I'm supposed to be able to always create
happiness, and right now I'm finding that very difficult.

Then I remembered that the goal is not to be happy
every minute of every day, or deny problems. The purpose
of the happiness habit is to be happy *most* of the time, to
be able to take control of the events of my life. Sometimes
feeling sadness, guilt, or anger is completely appropriate.
It alerts us to problems.

When I considered why I was feeling so low, I realized
that it was appropriate, and that I needed to take action

254

so the problem didn't recur. I used the problem-solving tool (the personal power page) to develop a plan of action. After creating a realistic and effective solution, I had a new and positive outlook on the future and the worry lifted.

The HabitBuilder Tool Chest is useful for turning problems into enjoyable challenges, and resolving problems effectively. Use it as needed—whether that's several times a day, once a week, or once a month.

Learning that *you* have the power and ability to develop solutions to your problems puts you in control of your life. If you use the tools in this section consistently over the next 90 days, you will expand your ability to handle adversity and gain the confidence and freedom to take on new and important challenges.

1. ***The Happiness Treasure Chest:*** This tool reminds you that cherishing the good in your life brings you more happiness.

2. ***Find the Pearl:*** If you look for it, there is something beneficial in every situation. This tool stops you from the destructive fixating on what's wrong, and propels you into putting your attention where it will be most rewarding and productive.

3. ***The Personal Power Page:*** When you are in the middle of a problem the emotion colors your thinking and it is hard to make wise decisions. By following each of the five steps in this

problem-solving tool you gain an objectivity about the situation. When you are able to detach from the problem you will come up with more effective long-term solutions. The more you use the five steps, the more you'll get into the habit of generating lasting solutions instead of quick fixes to problems that keep recurring.

Ways to Lift Your Mood

Some problems need to be thought out before taking action. A friend of mine was unhappy in her job and wanted to talk with her boss about it. Instead of barging in and blurting out her complaints, she took time to think about what she wanted to say, discussed it with some friends, and devised a plan of action. When she met with her boss, he was extremely impressed with what she said, and proposed a solution far better than she had even imagined. Her planning paid off.

However, many of us spend time worrying, fretting, fuming, and ruminating about things over which we have no control. This worrying is destructive to our well-being, as well as to those around us. Once I was teaching a customer service class and two of the participants were complaining bitterly about having to work weekends on a project. They felt it was unfair, and that management had made an unrealistic promise to a customer, causing them to have to work on Saturdays. They had been complaining for three weeks when they realized that their complaining was doing them no good, and it was only making them feel bad. There were going to have to do the project no matter what. The only choice they had was their attitude: they could be miserable or they could be cheerful. They chose to do the job cheerfully and, boy, were their co-workers happy!

Below are some are suggestions for lifting your mood when you find yourself worrying about something you can't do anything about, or in a low mood you want to get out of. Please add your favorite ways to enhance your mood.

1. Find a happiness buddy to share the process with.

2. Write about the situation for about 20 minutes.

3. Exercise.

4. Watch a comedy.

5. Do a good deed for someone else.

6. Sing out loud. (It is impossible to sing "Zip-a-Dee-Do-Dah" and remain depressed!)

7. Do something with a friend.

8. Pick an easy, small task and do it.

9. Change your attitude by focusing on something positive.

10. Read *Chicken Soup for the Soul*.

11. _____

12. _____

13. _____

1

The Happiness Treasure Chest

For children, playing pirates and hunting for buried treasure is a favorite game. Now, as adults, we don't want to spend time looking for someone else's treasure. We want to spend time creating our own treasure chest and filling it with the happiness of our lives.

Your treasure chest is a place to record things that make you happy. It can be a single word or a description of an event. For example, something that makes me smile is my daughter. Something else that made me happy was when a participant in a conflict resolution class shared how he used the skills to talk with his seven-year-old son instead of hitting him. A work event that was a joyous occasion was when a company I was working with took on a major improvement project and succeeded in reaching their goal.

You write in this section as you see those things that make you happy. Start off by writing at least ten things that make you happy today. Then add to it as time goes by.

Your treasure chest is to be used any time you feel in need of inspiration or encouragement, or when you simply want to savor the precious things in your life. It is your base, your anchor, your own private mirror reflecting the reality of your happiness. It should contain all that you have accomplished, all the events and occasions that have brought happiness to your heart.

The truth is, the happy get happier because they know how to be happy, and the troubled get more troubled because they pour all their life energy into their troubles.

– Susan Page, *How One of You Can Bring the Two of You Together*

The Happiness Treasure Chest

Things that make me happy ✦ Things that touch my heart
People I love, am glad to know, am glad to know about
Things I'm proud of ✦ Things I have accomplished
Things that make me smile or laugh out loud
Things I am happy that I have
Things I treasure ✦ Things I am grateful for

_____

_____

_____

_____

_____

_____

_____

_____

_____

_____

_____

*Let us each grasp a new idea this year.
Let us grasp the awareness of what it is
that makes us truly happy. Let us consider our personal preferences and learn
how to recognize, then embrace, moments
of happiness that are uniquely our own.*

– Sarah Ban Breathnach, *Simple Abundance*

1

The Happiness Treasure Chest

Things that make me happy ✦ Things that touch my heart
People I love, am glad to know, am glad to know about
Things I'm proud of ✦ Things I have accomplished
Things that make me smile or laugh out loud
Things I am happy that I have
Things I treasure ✦ Things I am grateful for

_____

_____

_____

_____

_____

_____

_____

_____

_____

_____

_____

_____

_____

One of the secrets of a happy life is continuous small treats.   – Iris Murdoch

The Happiness Treasure Chest

Things that make me happy ✦ Things that touch my heart
People I love, am glad to know, am glad to know about
Things I'm proud of ✦ Things I have accomplished
Things that make me smile or laugh out loud
Things I am happy that I have
Things I treasure ✦ Things I am grateful for

_____

_____

_____

_____

_____

_____

_____

_____

_____

_____

_____

_____

_____

_____

_____

_____

_____

_____

_____

_____

_____

_____

_____

_____

_____

_____

*If you cannot be
happy here and now,
you never will be.*

– Taisen Deshimaru

The Happiness Treasure Chest

Things that make me happy ✦ Things that touch my heart
People I love, am glad to know, am glad to know about
Things I'm proud of ✦ Things I have accomplished
Things that make me smile or laugh out loud
Things I am happy that I have
Things I treasure ✦ Things I am grateful for

_____

_____

_____

_____

_____

_____

_____

_____

_____

_____

_____

_____

_____

_____

*You can't prevent birds of sorrow
from flying over your head, but
you can prevent them from building
nests in your hair.*   – Chinese proverb

1

The Happiness Treasure Chest

Things that make me happy ✦ Things that touch my heart
People I love, am glad to know, am glad to know about
Things I'm proud of ✦ Things I have accomplished
Things that make me smile or laugh out loud
Things I am happy that I have
Things I treasure ✦ Things I am grateful for

_____

_____

_____

_____

_____

_____

_____

_____

_____

_____

_____

_____

_____

We can trust that our happiness will realign not only the dendrites in our brain but also the molecules of our material world and become a lullaby that will charm the universe.

– Barry Neil Kaufman

The Happiness Treasure Chest

Things that make me happy ✦ Things that touch my heart
People I love, am glad to know, am glad to know about
Things I'm proud of ✦ Things I have accomplished
Things that make me smile or laugh out loud
Things I am happy that I have
Things I treasure ✦ Things I am grateful for

_____

_____

_____

_____

_____

_____

_____

_____

_____

_____

_____

_____

2

Find the Pearl

*Like life between trapezes, the risks we
take in life can be wildly exhilarating or
wildly terrifying. Usually both. We choose
the label. We choose the experience.*

– Nicky Marone, *Women and Risk*

A pearl, one of nature's most beautiful gems, is created
from a grain of sand that finds its way into the shell of an
otherwise happy oyster. The grain of sand is an irritant.
Instead of getting upset, the oyster makes a chemical to
coat the sand so it is less of an annoyance. In time, a pearl
is produced.

Just as the oyster creates an object of beauty from an
irritating grain of sand, we too can make something better
out of adverse situations. When you find yourself perplexed
and vexed by a situation in your life, turn to this section.
Take a moment or two and describe the situation as you
see it. Then identify at least two positive things or benefits
that could, if looked at from a different perspective, come
from it. This may be difficult at first. You might want to
call a trusted friend to help you change your perspective.
But keep trying! It does get easier with practice!

2

Find the Pearl

In the space below, clearly describe the situation that is troubling you. In the space at right, identify at least two positive things about the situation and/or two possible positive outcomes. It may take some imagination and thinking, but you can do it. If you're stuck, you might call a friend and ask them for a positive take on the situation.

The Situation:

_____

_____

_____

_____

_____

_____

_____

_____

_____

_____

_____

_____

The Pearls:

_____

_____

_____

_____

_____

_____

_____

_____

_____

_____

_____

_____

_____

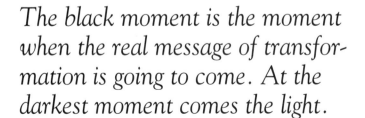

The black moment is the moment when the real message of transformation is going to come. At the darkest moment comes the light.

– Joseph Campbell

2

Find the Pearl

In the space below, clearly describe the situation that is troubling you. In the space at right, identify at least two positive things about the situation and/or two possible positive outcomes. It may take some imagination and thinking, but you can do it. If you're stuck, you might call a friend and ask them for a positive take on the situation.

The Situation:

_____

_____

_____

_____

_____

_____

_____

_____

_____

_____

_____

_____

The Pearls:

_____

_____

_____

_____

_____

_____

_____

_____

_____

_____

_____

_____

If you can bring yourself to apply your imagination to finding the possible favorable outcomes of undesired developments, even if only as an exercise, you'll see that it fosters creativity.

– Gavin de Becker, *The Gift of Fear*

2

Find the Pearl

In the space below, clearly describe the situation that is troubling you. In the space at right, identify at least two positive things about the situation and/or two possible positive outcomes. It may take some imagination and thinking, but you can do it. If you're stuck, you might call a friend and ask them for a positive take on the situation.

The Situation:

_____

_____

_____

_____

_____

_____

_____

_____

_____

_____

_____

_____

The Pearls:

_____

_____

_____

_____

_____

_____

_____

_____

_____

_____

_____

*No great improvements in the
lot of mankind are possible,
until a great change takes place
in the fundamental constitution
of their modes of thought.*

– John Stuart Mill

2

Find the Pearl

In the space below, clearly describe the situation that is troubling you. In the space at right, identify at least two positive things about the situation and/or two possible positive outcomes. It may take some imagination and thinking, but you can do it. If you're stuck, you might call a friend and ask them for a positive take on the situation.

The Situation:

_____

_____

_____

_____

_____

_____

_____

_____

_____

_____

_____

The Pearls:

_____

_____

_____

_____

_____

_____

_____

_____

_____

_____

_____

_____

_____

*Problems are like goldfish:
the more you feed them,
the bigger they get.*

– George Pransky, *Divorce is Not the Answer*

2

Find the Pearl

In the space below, clearly describe the situation that is troubling you. In the space at right, identify at least two positive things about the situation and/or two possible positive outcomes. It may take some imagination and thinking, but you can do it. If you're stuck, you might call a friend and ask them for a positive take on the situation.

The Situation:

_____

_____

_____

_____

_____

_____

_____

_____

_____

_____

_____

_____

_____

The Pearls:

_____

_____

_____

_____

_____

_____

_____

_____

_____

_____

_____

_____

_____

_____

The world is filled with people who have been handed the "worst" life has to offer . . . and they have come out winners!
— Susan Jeffers, Ph.D.,
Feel the Fear and Do It Anyway

2

Find the Pearl

In the space below, clearly describe the situation that is troubling you. In the space at right, identify at least two positive things about the situation and/or two possible positive outcomes. It may take some imagination and thinking, but you can do it. If you're stuck, you might call a friend and ask them for a positive take on the situation.

The Situation:

_____

_____

_____

_____

_____

_____

_____

_____

_____

_____

_____

_____

The Pearls:

_____

_____

_____

_____

_____

_____

_____

_____

_____

_____

_____

_____

_____

_____

Opportunity follows struggle.
It follows effort.
It follows hard work.
It doesn't come before.

– Shelby Steele

2

Find the Pearl

In the space below, clearly describe the situation that is troubling you. In the space at right, identify at least two positive things about the situation and/or two possible positive outcomes. It may take some imagination and thinking, but you can do it. If you're stuck, you might call a friend and ask them for a positive take on the situation.

The Situation:

_____

_____

_____

_____

_____

_____

_____

_____

_____

_____

_____

_____

_____

The Pearls:

_____

_____

_____

_____

_____

_____

_____

_____

_____

_____

_____

_____

_____

_____

The critical component to being productively positive is the ability to clearly confront the negative within a positive framework.

– James E. Loehr, *Stress to Success*

2

Find the Pearl

In the space below, clearly describe the situation that is troubling you. In the space at right, identify at least two positive things about the situation and/or two possible positive outcomes. It may take some imagination and thinking, but you can do it. If you're stuck, you might call a friend and ask them for a positive take on the situation.

The Situation:

_____

_____

_____

_____

_____

_____

_____

_____

_____

_____

_____

The Pearls:

It is not because things are difficult that we do not dare, it is because we do not dare that they are difficult.

– Seneca

2

Find the Pearl

In the space below, clearly describe the situation that is troubling you. In the space at right, identify at least two positive things about the situation and/or two possible positive outcomes. It may take some imagination and thinking, but you can do it. If you're stuck, you might call a friend and ask them for a positive take on the situation.

The Situation:

_____

_____

_____

_____

_____

_____

_____

_____

_____

_____

_____

The Pearls:

_____

_____

_____

_____

_____

_____

_____

_____

_____

_____

_____

_____

_____

_____

*Whenever they rebuild
an old building, they must
first destroy the old one.*

– Rumi, Persian Sufi poet

3

The Personal Power Page

The biggest problem that people have when they have a problem is not the problem itself, but rather their feelings about the problem. Confused? Let me explain. When we have a problem, we often spend our time and energy fretting, fuming, fussing, and worrying about it. Or we may spend time avoiding the problem, choosing to blame someone else for it, feeling angry about it, or conveniently forgetting about it.

To be alive is to have problems. In his book, *The Road Less Traveled*, Scott Peck begins with the simple statement: "Life is difficult." He goes on to say that the problem is not that life is difficult, but that we expect life to be easy. We wish our lives could be simple, problem-free, and devoid of any and all obstacles.

Our expectation that life is easy results in disappointment and annoyance when our reality turns out to be an unending series of daily crises and difficulties. We fight against our reality, grumbling and complaining about life as though it really should be easy and we should always be happy. Peck asserts that it is through the process of meeting life's daily challenges head-on, and solving them in a constructive manner, that life assumes meaning.

As a human relations expert, I've found that the best way for people to learn and retain knowledge is through simulated problem-resolution exercises. People grow when they are challenged. You will be a happier person if you confront your problems directly rather than finding ways to avoid them. Remember also that sometimes the resolution of a problem is the acceptance that there are some things that cannot be changed.

The personal power page is a five-step process for finding solutions to your problems. Use it whenever you have a dilemma to resolve. Remember, the more you use it, the more effectively it will work for you.

When you look at life and its many challenges as a test, or series of tests, you begin to see each issue you face as an opportunity to grow, a chance to roll with the punches.

– Richard Carlson, Ph.D.

3

The Personal Power Page

1. What is the problem or situation?

_____

_____

_____

2. What are three possible ways I can solve the problem?

_____

_____

_____

_____

_____

_____

_____

3. Here is what I am going to do about it:

_____

_____

_____

_____

4. When am I going to start doing it?

_____

_____

_____

5. What did I learn from this problem?

_____

_____

_____

_____

_____

_____

_____

_____

Acceptance of what has happened is the first step in overcoming the consequences of any misfortune.

– William James

3

The Personal Power Page

1. What is the problem or situation?

_____

_____

_____

2. What are three possible ways I can solve the problem?

_____

_____

_____

_____

_____

_____

_____

3. Here is what I am going to do about it:

_____

_____

_____

_____

4. When am I going to start doing it?

_____

_____

_____

5. What did I learn from this problem?

_____

_____

_____

_____

_____

_____

_____

_____

The first skill you must acquire is the ability to immediately sense when adversity is happening.

– Paul G. Stoltz, Ph.D., *Adversity Quotient*

The Personal Power Page

1. What is the problem or situation?

_____

_____

_____

2. What are three possible ways I can solve the problem?

_____

_____

_____

_____

_____

_____

_____

3. Here is what I am going to do about it:

_____

_____

_____

_____

4. When am I going to start doing it?

_____

_____

_____

5. What did I learn from this problem?

_____

_____

_____

_____

_____

_____

_____

_____

_____

Something almost magical happens when people break through the obstacles that hold them back and discover what is truly inside them.

– Brian D. Biro

3

The Personal Power Page

1. What is the problem or situation?

_____

_____

_____

2. What are three possible ways I can solve the problem?

_____

_____

_____

_____

_____

_____

3. Here is what I am going to do about it:

_____

_____

_____

_____

4. When am I going to start doing it?

_____

_____

_____

5. What did I learn from this problem?

_____

_____

_____

_____

_____

_____

_____

All the world's teachers and trainers combined cannot teach you a fraction of what you can teach yourself.

– Art Niemann

3

The Personal Power Page

1. What is the problem or situation?

_____

_____

_____

2. What are three possible ways I can solve the problem?

_____

_____

_____

_____

_____

_____

_____

3. Here is what I am going to do about it:

_____

_____

_____

_____

4. When am I going to start doing it?

_____

_____

_____

5. What did I learn from this problem?

_____

_____

_____

_____

_____

_____

_____

_____

_____

_____

Kites rise highest against the wind, not with it.

– Winston Churchill

3

The Personal Power Page

1. What is the problem or situation?

_____

_____

_____

2. What are three possible ways I can solve the problem?

_____

_____

_____

_____

_____

_____

3. Here is what I am going to do about it:

_____

_____

_____

_____

4. When am I going to start doing it?

_____

_____

_____

5. What did I learn from this problem?

_____

_____

_____

_____

_____

_____

_____

_____

_____

In all of my experience, I have never seen lasting solutions to problems, lasting happiness and success, that came from the outside in.

– Stephen Covey

3

The Personal Power Page

1. What is the problem or situation?

_____

_____

_____

2. What are three possible ways I can solve the problem?

_____

_____

_____

_____

_____

_____

3. Here is what I am going to do about it:

_____

_____

_____

_____

4. When am I going to start doing it?

_____

_____

_____

5. What did I learn from this problem?

_____

_____

_____

_____

_____

_____

_____

A myth is a fixed way of looking at the world which cannot be destroyed because, looked at through the myth, all evidence supports that myth.

– Edward de Bono

APPENDIX

The 13 characteristics of happy people was developed from these well-documented and researched sources.

1. **Happy people like themselves**
   The Pursuit of Happiness, David G. Myers, Ph.D.

2. **Happy people are optimistic**
   The Pursuit of Happiness, David G. Myers, Ph.D.
   Learned Optimism, Martin E. P. Seligman, Ph.D.
   Feel the Fear and Do It Anyway, Susan Jeffers, Ph.D.

3. **Happy people are outgoing**
   The Pursuit of Happiness, David G. Myers, Ph.D.

4. **Happy people believe they are in control of their lives**
   The Pursuit of Happiness, David G. Myers, Ph.D.
   The Book of You, Bernard Asbell
   Brain Lock, Jeffrey M.Schwartz, M.D.

5. **Happy people are friendly**
   The Pursuit of Happiness, David G. Myers, Ph.D.
   Flow: The Psychology of Optimal Experience, Mihaly Csikszentmihalyi

6. **Happy people know that the best things in life are free**
   Flow: The Psychology of Optimal Experience, Mihaly Csikszentmihalyi

7. **Happy people find a reason to laugh**

    Anatomy of An Illness, Norman Cousins

    The Healing Power of Humor, Allen Klein

    What You Can Change and What You Can't, Martin
    E.P. Seligman, Ph.D.

8. **Happy people experience "the flow" in their work**

    Flow: The Psychology of Optimal Experience, Mihaly
    Csikszentmihalyi

    Finding Flow, Mihaly Csikszentmihalyi

9. **Happy people spread their joy**

    Why Marriages Succeed or Fail, John Gottman, Ph.D.

    Gung Ho! Ken Blanchard, Sheldon Bowles

10. **Happy people control their impulses**

    Emotional Intelligence, Daniel Goleman

    Brain Lock, Jeffrey M.Schwartz, M.D.

    The Road Less Traveled, M. Scott Peck

11. **Happy people know that love makes the world go round**

    The Pursuit of Happiness, David G. Myers, Ph.D.

    Flow: The Psychology of Optimal Experience, Mihaly
    Csikszentmihalyi

12. **Happy people are enthusiastic**

    Ralph Waldo Emerson

    Beyond Success, Brian Biro

13. **Happy people know what their life is all about**

    The Pursuit of Happiness, David G. Myers, Ph.D

    Flow: The Psychology of Optimal Experience, Mihaly
    Csikszentmihalyi

    When All You've Ever Wanted Isn't Enough, Rabbi
    Harold Kushner

REFERENCES

Allen, Roger E. and Stephan. *Winnie the Pooh on Problem-Solving*. New York: Penguin Books, 1995.

Argyris, Chris. *Knowledge for Action*. San Francisco: Jossey Bass Inc., 1993.

Asbell, Bernard. *The Book of You*. New York: Fawcett Columbine, 1997.

Beck, Aaron T. *Love Is Never Enough*. New York: Harper & Row, 1988.

Bolton, Robert. *People Skills*. New York: Touchstone, 1986.

Burns, David M. *The Feeling Good Handbook*. New York: Plume, 1990.

Carlson, Richard. *Don't Sweat the Small Stuff, and It's All Small Stuff*. New York: Hyperion, 1997.

Csikszentmihalyi, Mihaly. *Finding Flow*. New York: Basic Books, 1997.

Cousins, Norman. *Head First*. New York: E. P. Dutton, 1989.

Covey, Stephen R. *First Things First*. New York: Fireside Books, 1994.

Covey, Stephen R. *The Seven Habits of Highly Effective People*. New York: Fireside Books, 1990.

Cudney, Milton R. and Robert E. Hardy. *Self-Defeating Behaviors*. New York: Harper Collins, 1993.

Dawes, Robyn M. *House of Cards*. New York: The Free Press, 1996.

De Becker, Gavin. *The Gift of Fear*. Boston: Little & Brown, 1997.

Ellis, Albert and Robert A. Harper. *A New Guide to Rational Living*. North Hollywood: Wilshire Book Company, 1975.

Frankl, Viktor E. *Man's Search for Meaning*. New York: Touchstone, 1984.

Franklin, Benjamin. Edited by George Rogers. *The Art of Virtue*. Eden Praire, Minnesota: Acorn Press, 1996.

Gallwey, W. Timothy. *The Inner Game of Tennis*. New York: Random House, 1974.

Gillett, Richard. *Change Your Mind, Change Your World*. New York: Fireside Books, 1992.

Goldman, Daniel. *Emotional Intelligence*. New York: Bantam Books, 1995.

Gottman, John. *Why Marriages Succeed or Fail*. New York: Fireside Books, 1994.

Greene, Bob and Oprah Winfrey. *Make the Connection*. New York: Hyperion, 1996.

Hanks, Kurt and Gerreld L. Pulsipher. *Five Secrets to Personal Productivity*. Salt Lake City: The Franklin Quest, 1993.

Jeffers, Susan. *Feel the Fear and Do It Anyway*. New York: Fawcett Columbine, 1987.

Kaufman, Barry Neil. *Happiness Is a Choice*. New York: Random House, 1994.

Kusher, Harold. *When All You Ever Wanted Isn't Enough*. New York: Summit Books, 1986.

Lerner, Harriet G. *The Dance of Intimacy*. New York: Harper Perennial, 1990.

Loehr, James E. *Stress for Success*. New York: Times Books, 1997.

Maltz, Maxwell. *Psycho-Cybernetics*. New York: Pocket Books, 1960.

Marone, Nicky. *Women and Risk*. New York: St. Martin's Press, 1992.

May, Rollo. *The Courage to Create*. New York: Bantam Books, 1975.

McGinnis, Alan Loy. *Bringing Out the Best In People*. Minneapolis: Augsburg Publishing House, 1985.

Myers, David G. *The Pursuit of Happiness*. New York: Avon Books, 1992.

Niemann, Art. *The Ultimate Lesson*. Los Angeles: SLI Press, 1996.

Page, Susan. *How One of You Can Bring The Two of You Together*. New York: Broadway Books, 1997.

Pearsall, Paul. *The Pleasure Prescription*. Alameda, California: Hunter House, 1996.

Peck, M. Scott. *The Road Less Traveled*. New York: Simon and Schuster, 1978.

Peck, M. Scott. *Further Along the Road Less Traveled*. New York: Simon and Schuster, 1993.

Peters, Tom. *The Pursuit of Wow*. New York: Vintage Books, 1994.

Pitino, Rick. *Success Is a Choice*. New York: Broadway Books, 1997.

Price, Pritchett. *Mind Shift*. Dallas: Price Pritchett, 1996.

Schlessinger, Laura. *How Could You Do That?* New York: Harper Perennial, 1997.

Schwartz, Jeffrey. *Brain Lock*. New York: Harper Collins, 1997.

Schwartz, Tony. *What Really Matters*. New York: Bantam Books, 1996.

Seligman, Martin E. P. *Learned Optimism*. New York: Pocket-Books, 1992.

Seligman, Martin E. P. *What You Can Change and What You Can't*. New York: Alfred A. Knopf, 1993.

Seligman, Martin E. P., with Karen Revivich, Lisa Jaycox, and Jane Gillham. *The Optimistic Child*. New York: Harper Perennial, 1996.

Senge, Peter. *The Fifth Discipline*. New York: Doubleday, 1990.

Stoltz, Paul G. *Adversity Quotient*. New York: John Wiley & Sons, 1997.

Telushkin, Joseph. *Words That Hurt, Words That Heal*. New York: William Morrow & Co., 1996.

Wheatley, Margaret J. *Leadership and the New Science*. San Francisco: Berrett-Koehler, 1992.

Wheelis, Allen. *How People Change*. New York: Harper & Row, 1973.

White, Richard M. Jr. *The Entrepreneur's Manual*. Radnor, Pennsylvania: Chilton, 1977.

Williamson, Marianne. *A Return to Love*. New York: Harper Spotlight, 1993.

Zadra, Dan, with Katie Lambert. *Little Miracles*. Edmonds, Washington: Compendium, Ind.

Your Comments Are Wanted

We want to make sure that you are as happy as possible, and your comments on what you love about this program and suggestions for improvement are critical to reaching that goal. We would appreciate your taking a few minutes to tell us about some of the results you have gotten by choosing the happiness habit, as well as what worked well for you and what would make it even better. Thank you so much for taking the time to let us know what you think. That makes us very happy!

1. Results I have gotten by choosing the happiness habit:

_____

_____

_____

2. What worked well for me: _____

_____

_____

_____

3. What would make it even better: _____

_____

_____

_____

You can fax this to us at (760) 771-9618, or mail it to:
Roedway Press, P.O. Box 903, La Quinta, CA 92253

Order Form

CALL TOLL-FREE: (888) MY-HABIT, (888) 694-2248
Please have your credit card available.

FAX this order form to (760) 771-9618

MAIL this form to Roedway Press,
P.O. Box 903, La Quinta, CA 92253

Please send me _____ copies of *Choose the Happiness Habit*

    Enclosed is $14.95 per book   _____

    California residents add 7.75% sales tax   _____

    Shipping & handling: $4 for the first book,
    plus $2 for each additional book   _____

    Total enclosed: _____

Mail to: _____

_____

_____

_____

❐ Enclosed is my check.

Please bill my:
❐ Visa   Card # _____
❐ MasterCard
❐ Amex   Expires_____
❐ Discover   Name on card _____

Thank you!

*Please call to find out about discounts
for orders over 10 books.*

Order Form

CALL TOLL-FREE: (888) MY-HABIT, (888) 694-2248
Please have your credit card available.

FAX this order form to (760) 771-9618

MAIL this form to Roedway Press,
P.O. Box 903, La Quinta, CA 92253

Please send me _____ copies of *Choose the Happiness Habit*

Enclosed is $14.95 per book _____

California residents add 7.75% sales tax _____

Shipping & handling: $4 for the first book,
plus $2 for each additional book _____

Total enclosed: _____

Mail to: _____

_____

_____

_____

❐ Enclosed is my check.

Please bill my:

❐ Visa   Card # _____

❐ MasterCard
❐ Amex   Expires _____

❐ Discover   Name on card _____

Thank you!

*Please call to find out about discounts
for orders over 10 books.*